AN OPEN LOOK

TWIGGY

AN OPEN LOOK

TWIGGY'S GUIDE TO

LOOKING AND

FEELING GREAT

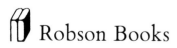 Robson Books

Text arranged and researched: Angela Neustatter
Editor: Neville Shulman
Line Drawings: Sharon Finmark
Design: Anne Davison
Design assistant: Christine Copsey

Every care has been taken in preparing the diets and exercises in this book, but readers should have regard to their age and state of health before following them. If you are in doubt about their suitability for you, consult your medical advisor, as no responsibility can be accepted by the author or publishers.

FIRST PUBLISHED IN GREAT BRITAIN IN 1985 BY ROBSON BOOKS LTD., BOLSOVER HOUSE, 5-6 CLIPSTONE STREET, LONDON W1P 7EB. COPYRIGHT   1985 LESLEY ARMSTRONG.

British Library Cataloguing in Publication Data

Twiggy
An Open Look
 1. Beauty, Personal
 I. Title
 646.7′2′1088042   RA778

 ISBN 0-86051-324-6

Printed in Hungary

This book is dedicated to all the children in the world, but especially my daughter Carly

CONTENTS

ACKNOWLEDGEMENTS

I want to give my very warm thanks to all those who have helped in putting this book together, particularly Angela Neustatter for her diligent research, Alison Field for all the hard work she too put into it, Neville Shulman for his industrious editorship and Susan Rea for her behind-the-scenes contribution.

Barbara Daly for her special make-up contribution; John Swannell for some stunning photographs; Sue Snell for finding wonderful clothes and accessories to use in them.

Barbara Hulanicki for the gorgeous clothes designed over many years, and for the stories she remembered, the printable ones that is; Joan Price of The Face Place for her invaluable help, Christiana in New York for her beauty hints; Karen Tamburelli for her patient teachings of difficult dance routines.

Warm thanks to you all, and to the many, many others.

INTRODUCTION

This book won't provide you with that elusive key to open the doors to beauty, success, fame, and fortune, that so many others seem to promise, because I don't have it. If you think you have it, then you should write a book, please, and put me down for a copy or two. Quite frankly, I don't believe you can learn how to become beautiful and healthy from books alone; it takes rather more effort than that – but I do believe you can receive a push in the right direction – from seeing how others plan their lives and routines, and that is what I hope you will gain from my book.

When I was asked to put together my own book on beauty, health and fashion, my first reaction was that surely there are too many already, and why add to the number? I then read and looked at most of those that are around, and realized that none of them were using an approach I really cared for, and that maybe there were others who agreed with me and wanted to read a book of this kind which did not adopt too dogmatic an attitude to these subjects, and allowed the readers to develop their own way of progressing, and at their own pace.

The emphasis in the books I read was that the reader must take totally seriously every little idea mentioned, every nuance uttered, follow them rigorously and in effect try to clone herself, or himself, on the writer, without allowing for their individual personalities, shapes and sizes, and in effect probably try to be something they were not.

Most people are given something special in life, whether it is beautiful hair, a great figure, a musical talent, personality, above-average brains, an intriguing voice; and the secret to some success, on whatever level, is to find out what that special ingredient is, and use it to its fullest potential. Some people think I am good-looking, others would say I'm too skinny, some think I

can sing or dance, others only like classical artists – it's all a matter of choice. All I know is that the more I meet famous people, whether those born with titles and money, or those who have become great actors and actresses, tremendous dancers and singers, the more I realize that it really *is* a case of the fickle finger of fate (always trying to remember the reverse case is also very true – there but for the grace of God go I.)

So I decided it would be good to put together some of the things, ideas and pointers, which over the years, have been useful and helpful in making me look and feel good, and which I believe can be adopted and adapted by anyone. This is not a book which will tell you, or show you, step by step what to do to end up looking like me. Far more fun is to end up looking like a re-vamped you!

It has been said that I became popular because I could be anyone's daughter; and that lots of girls thought that, with a bit of luck, they could be me. I don't know if that's true or not, but the point is basically my looks are quite straightforward yet – because I got swept into the modelling world very young – I learnt a number of techniques and ideas for creating all kinds of images with my looks. I also learnt the importance of valuing and looking after one's natural assets.

Well, none of this is exclusive to me. Any of you can do the same, whether you are slim like me, tall, large, short, or curvaceous or a combination of all those. We all have good things which can be emphasized and made the most of, and this is one of the basic points of my book. I really don't go for all these disciplinarian health guides, with their quest for the perfect body, the perfect look, whereby you are expected to become obsessed with a daily exercise régime, a diet of self-denial, and a rigorous life-style which cuts out all frivolity, fun, and even being self-indulgent – sometimes, that is. I don't have the willpower or even the will to live like that. Looking good and being healthy are very important, but so is the enjoyment of life, and I have seen far too many people dedicating themselves to trying to achieve some impossible goal – exercising half their day, eating extraordinary things, or practically nothing, slavishly following some make-up plan supposed to make them look like their heroine. Of course it doesn't happen, because you cannot make yourself into someone completely different. And, unfortunately, many people do become very miserable making supreme efforts to follow what someone has laid down in a book; usually someone who does not lead a normal and ordinary life – which is preferable, I can assure you, to life on a roller-coaster for it has to end some time, and often does so unhappily.

I suppose I was lucky to learn so young about playing with my image by using clothes and accessories, and I learned how liberating it is to be able to feel like someone different every day. It's the same with my hair or make-up. I would hate to have a definite look which was *me,* and which had to be the same all the time. My emphasis all the time is on being versatile and changing to suit a mood or a special event.

The secret, if there is one, is to just have a sound approach to basic health and go from there. Mind you, I feel pretty funny saying all this, and don't think I'm preaching to the world! Certainly not, I'm not one of those Hollywood glamour types with an elaborate beauty régime, a hoard of secrets for disguising flaws, for looking younger, for putting on a make-up mask. I believe in letting my freckles show and half the time I hardly wear any make-up – I believe it's important to like yourself as you are, and that's why being fit and looking after your skin is far more important than knowing how to disguise the lines and age signs we all get as we grow older.

I looked at the pictures John Swannell took of me especially for the book, and my first reaction was, 'Gosh, I do look mature – and about time too,' and I really meant that. I don't look like the sixteen-year-old skinny model anymore and although I loved that time and enjoyed it very much, I have moved on a long way and matured a lot since, and that image now needs to be apparent from the latest photographs of me.

I really feel sorry for those who are haunted by the idea of being older, especially of looking older. One wonderful lady who is now middle-aged, known for her stunning looks, had all the flaws touched out of the book she had published. Such a pity, I think, because she is so interesting and in any case she's still gorgeous.

I couldn't and wouldn't hide my age, anyway. Of course, it's been written in the press so many times that anyone who wants to can easily work out my age now, and when I shall be forty and

fifty – and good luck to them. I don't share the view that getting older is a process of loss – I think it should be looked at as a process of gaining. I love knowing more, being more confident than I was as a teenager and a twenty-year-old.

I have got together some information which I think is worthwhile and can be followed reasonably – for example I think it is worthwhile understanding the basis of sensible diet. Ever since I became a mother I've felt it very important to understand the effects of the food we eat, which vitamins and minerals matter, the way different foods can provide energy or alter the body's function, so all that is in. I've also included a range of different diets from a high energy one to a slimming one, so you can choose which you might like. But I am not suggesting an ideal body weight, or that you should try to become my shape – I just happen to have been born very slim, and have remained so, no matter what I eat, and it obviously wouldn't be right for everyone to be this size.

There's also a whole chapter on dance, not just because it is good for you – which it is – but because it has given me such enormous pleasure, as well as doing wonders for the shape of my calves, for the first time in my life! When I was offered the part in the Gershwin musical *My One And Only* which of course took me to Broadway for nearly two years, I had to go into a tough training programme to learn tap and other dance steps. It was very very hard work, because I had to practice sometimes eight hours a day – I wouldn't suggest you do that – and although it was immensely hard I was amazed at how strong and fit my body became, and incredibly supple. Since then I have been able to use it to an extent I had never imagined possible before.

I have also written a lot about clothes, not only because they are a great passion of mine, but also because I think they are one of the key ways in which you can quickly alter your image. It is just startling what different effects can be created. For example, I recently bought a truly wonderful, shocking-pink skin-tight

leather skirt and a Marilyn Monroe top to go with it – you'll see a photograph of it in the book – and I can wear the whole outfit very dressed up, with high heels, dangly earrings, hair piled on my head, or I can wear just the top with jeans and sneakers. I have some leather riding breeches with which I can put high pumps, a skimpy antique blouse and perhaps a big scarf, or I wear them with high boots, a tailored jacket and a big polo neck sweater.

Being a mother of course has been one of the most important things in my life. It adds a few lines; and I've had my share of a few stresses and they must show, but I don't care in the slightest, I'll keep on trying to look good, and I hope you will as well.

F A S H I O N

CLOTHES are one of my passions. I enjoyed dressing up an early age and I still receive the same, childlike delight from dressing up in something new, or indeed in something old. I keep most of my old clothes and it gives me a real buzz sometimes to pull out a dress I wore ten years ago and team it with a new garment. It can be enormous fun playing games with the way you look, transforming your appearance according to mood and whim. Particularly nowadays, when there are no hard and fast fashion rules.

I know people who will one day be amazingly chic and smart in, perhaps, a tailored suit and high heels, and the next day they will dress in dungarees and a sweat shirt. And that's an enjoyable way to use clothes. I don't believe in the doctrinaire approach to fashion which says that we should always wear the latest look, and that certain designers are to be followed absolutely. That's dull and it takes away any inventiveness.

This is me putting on the style! Fortunately fashion is no longer bound by hard and fast rules. That's what makes it so much fun.

The younger designers in Britain and America are making clothes which are far more relaxed, more inventive, much closer to the ideas coming off the street than we have seen in the past. Take companies like PX and Body Map, they are very much attuned to the iconoclastic taste of today's young people. In fact, Body Map was asked to design all the costumes for the dance troupe of Michael Clark, a man who has an amazing individual rock style of dancing, and who has been called one of the very best choreographers in Britain.

Then of course there are the talented designers like Katherine Hamnett, who is British but sells in America. She invented the sexy, tough, utilitarian look – parachute suits in silk, loose, zippered trousers, big masculine jackets with wonderful detail. Her designs have been copied all over the world. Betty Jackson is another person designing lovely avant-garde clothes, and then there are people like Bridget Woods and Chrissie Walsh who have gone into dance-inspired clothes.

In America there is less emphasis on the very casual, street-derived clothes, but designers like Anne Klein, Ralph Lauren and Norma Kamali make relaxed, classical-style clothes which can be worn in many different ways and do not dictate an absolute style. Clothes by contemporary designers from all the important fashion countries – France, Italy, Britain, America and Japan – can be worn exactly as the designer has visualized, and as is shown at the collections, or can be combined inventively with other garments. It all makes the business of fashion such fun. I call this progress.

I may have been a model but I have never felt that clothes should be taken too seriously. To me the fun of clothes is to do just as you wish with them. Something which puzzles me, and I've noticed it particularly over the past years, is a kind of puritanism some people have towards the idea of dressing up. The argument seems to be that clothes are frivolous and that women shouldn't preoccupy themselves with their appearance. Well, I have no time for that. I think it's perfectly possible to be interested and involved in many important things and still enjoy dressing up. Besides, I believe it's creative to put yourself together well and to look interesting for other people.

I remember the party I organized for a friend's birthday. I decided that we should hold it in a Mexican restaurant in New York. I thought it would be fun to have a really festive event. I suggested that everyone should dress up in Mexican style. I bought myself a wonderful dress, all white frills and flounces, very full and flamboyant – the kind of thing Bardot used to wear. I did my hair in a very curly style and added lots of flowers, and I wore high heels. It was great fun being so dressed up, and such an

(Opposite) **Feeling really comfortable and casual. Great leather jodhpurs and an antique blouse. By the way, you may not realize that 'jodhpur' comes from the name of the polo-playing Indian city of Jodhpur.**

enjoyable contrast to the day-to-day utilitarian clothes.

It is important to dress up sometimes. That utilitarian, sporty look that came into vogue during the Seventies went too far. I thought it very sad when the Savoy Hotel in London agreed to let people in wearing jeans! It seemed to symbolize the end of dressing up, and people would go to parties just in jeans – very dull. I am delighted that the Eighties has seen a return to a more stylish look.

One night in New York I had to dress up to receive the annual Miss Ziegfield award and although I quite often wear smart pants – satin, velvet or leather – in the evenings, I wanted something that would really match the grandeur of the occasion. I was lucky to find an American theatrical designer, Dona Granata, who is very good at thinking up something really special. We discussed a few ideas. Anyone having a garment made should have a few thoughts of her own, rather than just handing over completely to somebody else. Dona came up with an amazing dress in gold lamé cloth, just like liquid gold. It is almost mediaeval-looking with a full skirt, a very tight bodice and big puffed sleeves. I felt very spoiled wearing such a wonderful garment that night, because I don't often buy many terribly expensive clothes.

For a long time now my regular day wear has been jeans, or casual pants, worn with sweaters and shirts. I particularly like the loose-fitting style which came in with the whole health cult. In winter, I tend to wear turtle or crew neck-style sweaters with straight jeans, a simple, neat look which is warm too. In summer, I might well go for shorts or loose trousers teamed with a T-shirt. I did have a phase when I tired of pants and tops. I actually felt rather dowdy in them. It was summer in New York and I decided it would make a change to dress more femininely, to be more in tune with the bright sunny weather. I started wearing antique dresses and lots of little white cotton dresses trimmed with embroidery and lace. These clothes look lovely and wash so easily.

I really enjoyed looking feminine and still do. It's too easy to get into the habit of wearing jeans all the time and never to dress in pretty clothes. But I wouldn't wear clothes which actually inhibited my life-style. I wouldn't, for example, wear delicate crêpe de Chine or a fabric which required dry-cleaning except for special occasions. My clothes have to be suitable for rollicking around with my daughter Carly, for dashing around town, doing the shopping – generally leading an active, busy life.

Many people stick to one particular style of dressing and find it hard to change. I think it's important to make the effort occasionally to try something new. I suggest going out and

(Opposite) **I fell in love with this beautiful yellow suede jacket the moment I saw it, and just had to have it. Perfect for special occasions when I don't want to look too dressed up.**

buying two or three really different outfits – the kind of things you have never worn before but have admired from afar. Obviously, you must try them on before buying, and make sure you take a really candid look at yourself too – nobody looks good in absolutely everything. I know some clothes don't suit me at all, even though they look terrific on others. So be cautious. If you think the outfit looks good, but you feel nervous at the idea of *you* in that garment, don't buy. Don't waste money on something which you know you just wouldn't wear. But do try to be a bit braver each time you buy something new and see if you can enjoy it. You might get masses of compliments! By enlarging your repertoire of looks you are on the way to learning to develop a varied and enjoyable style. A lot of people lack the confidence to dress up, and justify it by saying that clothes don't interest them. Yet it seems strange to me that something that plays such a big part of our lives, something as significant as how we appear to the world, can be uninteresting.

Of course, all this is fine as long as you like the body you are going to hang clothes on to. This is important and so it is essential that your body is healthy and well exercised. People of all shapes and sizes can look good if they care for their bodies so that they have firm flesh, good posture, a look of vigour about them. It is a cliché, but very true, that knowing you look after yourself makes you look good to the world.

Dresses full of embroidery and lace are just right for summer dreaming.

I have met many well-known personalities, not at all raving beauties, who are famous for their beauty and style. In fact, many people who are praised for their looks when they are made-up and photographed, are just pleasant-looking women who have learned to style themselves up and who care for their bodies. The most inexpensive, ordinary clothes can be attractive on a nice, fit body, whereas the best-designed outfit in the world won't look good if you slouch, hunch your shoulders, and your stomach sticks out.

Large people tend to worry about dressing up, as though they have no right to aim for glamour. Yet I think a large, well-shaped body can look quite devastating in the right clothes. The times I have longed to have more bust, more curves, so that I could wear low-cut, film star dresses! Bigger women often have wonderful busts and hips, but again it is posture that is all-important. People who dislike being large may hunch their shoulders, and let their body slouch, and then nothing looks good. But the larger person who exercises to keep the stomach flat, and holds herself well, can leave the thin ones like me looking positively insignificant.

I have a friend who wears flamboyant dresses with lots of décolletage. She wears very loose-fitting, beautifully embroidered and decorated ethnic dresses, usually with a quite neat, well-fitted yoke. She wears shoes with a slight heels and tends to pile her rather unruly, curly hair on top of her head. And she always looks marvellously exotic and lovely. I have also seen very tall people, who clearly feel self-conscious about their appearance, look stunning when they abandon discreet clothes designed to make them less conspicuous. A slinky antique crêpe dress or a very full, vivid skirt and silk T-shirt can look fantastic. And in summer, nobody looks better than the tall person in Bermuda shorts and flat sandals.

People often say, well, it's okay for you, you're very slim. But I haven't always felt comfortable about my shape. There was a time when being skinny wasn't fashionable. I can remember as a teenager being constantly teased. It wasn't until I started modelling, when I was 'discovered', that I came to terms with my body. Then suddenly I was 'the shape'; everyone wanted to be my size and of course clothes in the Sixties were made with the young, under-developed look in mind. So I was very lucky because that helped me to accept the way I looked.

I was fortunate to have been modelling at a time when all the fashion rules were being broken down. After years of *haute couture* and formal design, suddenly came what I call 'belly-laugh' clothes, clothes designed to put a thumb to the nose at serious fashion. The clothes which Barbara Hulanicki, Mary Quant and so many others made were designed to be fun, liberating, a break with seriousness. They were clothes to be stylish and individual in. You didn't have to wear them a certain way or with particular accessories.

I remember Diana Vreeland saying some years ago: 'Style is everything, style is the most important word.' And I couldn't agree more. So many people are finding that they can try out clothes which they like without being considered eccentric or inappropriate. The fashion rules have broken down sufficiently now for unorthodox dress to be accepted everywhere.

Simple specs, hairslide, an original look that started the fashion upheaval.

MY STYLE OF FASHION

MY wardrobe is a real nostalgia trip. I am a hoarder. I keep my clothes a long time. There is a myth that models and show-biz people throw everything out each season and re-fill their closets with all the newest styles. Some may do that, but I certainly don't.

I do have a periodic weed-out when I get rid of clothes which I really don't like, which I absolutely cannot imagine putting on again. I'm prepared to believe that they have outlived cupboard space. Like most people I have impulse buys, which seem great at the time but are a disaster once you put them on at home in front of a mirror which is not as kind as those in the shops. Nor is there an assistant urging you on, saying how wonderful madam looks! These peccadillos go, but I do like to keep any of my clothes I have really enjoyed wearing or which represent an era of my life I want to recall.

I take the view that clothes which I have enjoyed wearing, which represent a time or event in my life that was important or great fun, are like old chums and deserve to be kept.

I have quite a few pairs of trousers because they are the garment I wear more than any other. I wear them in the day time and for going out in the evenings. My basics are good quality, well-cut jeans in the traditional, straight-leg style, essential for anyone who feel they look good in jeans. They have five times the life of ordinary fabric trousers because of course they still

(Opposite) **Frills and flounces, and so, so feminine. This dress was just right for the theatre, both on stage and off.**

23

Well-cut jeans in a classic straight-leg style can look good for years. But be ruthless about disgarding them when the cut begins to sag, or people will think the sag is you.

look terrific when they get old and battered. I'm not really interested in variations of jeans – they go in and out of fashion too fast. Bell bottoms or cut-off jeans, for example, look rather weird now their time has passed.

There is a myth that trousers only look good on slim or perfectly-proportioned people, but this just isn't true. Trousers can also look good on large people, people with rounded bottoms, provided they are a really neat fit – but not so neat that the body's lines of flesh are revealed. The secret to buying trousers is to try on a lot of different makes, and when you find a brand name which really works for your body, stick to it. It's amazing how different two pairs of jeans can be. And it's the same with sizes – a size ten by one manufacturer, for example, will be much smaller than that by another manufacturer. And it tends to be true that the cheapest makes are the skimpiest.

It's worthwhile buying, perhaps, a couple of inexpensive pairs of high fashion pants in a season and wearing them a lot, then discarding them when the style changes. It's worth comparing prices of similar items in, for example, the small exclusive shops in the smart streets of London or New York with the chain stores and the department stores. You may find a similar garment at a very different price. When buying something as expensive as leather trousers, it is sensible to have them made up. Most of us buy something really pricey like this only very occasionally, and my feeling is that for a relatively small extra amount they can be made-to-measure in exactly the skin you want. Leather trousers are a big investment at the time, but once you have them they are with you forever. Leather doesn't wear out and as with jeans – only more so – they look great when a bit battered and worn.

I have light tops and sweaters in many different plain colours – I know some people like to choose a couple of basic colours and build their wardrobe around them, but I enjoy wearing a variety of shades. I try to pick out the colour of my top with my footwear, with a belt, ear-rings or leg-warmers. I think an outfit looks much more interesting if you do give the colours some cohesion. I also have some large sloppy sweaters which go well with tight trousers or leggings, and I like the way they look with long, full skirts – a homespun look but pleasant.

I like blouses very much. Barbara Hulanicki, who ran London's Biba store in the Sixties, has made some of my favourite blouses. I was lucky that she began designing in the era when my shape was fashionable. Those wonderfully precise, slim-cut dresses and separates were the kind of things I felt really comfortable wearing. And I suppose that isn't surprising as I have the shape which Barbara had in mind when she conceived the Biba styles.

It's a case of hats you win! A
great way to change your look
and mood and image.

She isn't designing for the commercial market at present but I'm very fortunate because she will still make things up for me. In fact, she's like a fairy godmother. I phone her up days – hours even sometimes – before I need something and she always manages to get it done in time. I know that I can trust her to get it right. And I get involved too. I always talk through with her the design she has in mind. We have such a long-standing friendship that we share feelings, nerves and jokes. Because I quite often get nervous before an event, I rely on her to give me a boost. I can get up on stage and perform because I know what is expected of me, but I find it very different going into a room full of people I don't know. I can feel like a rather shy, awkward kid amongst very confident and successful people.

It's worth looking out for someone who will make up clothes for you – if you cannot do it yourself, that is. It's surprising how often there seems to be absolutely nothing in the shops you really like and so you can end up buying things you only half-like. If you have a friend who is a good dressmaker and keen to make a bit of money, why not find a pattern, or even sketch up a design of your own, and have it made?

Barbara has a superb eye for colour. She made me realize that I can wear very bright, vivid colours. There's this idea that blondes should stick to pastel colours or black, but I adore really bright pinks, greens, blues, purples. I have a marvellous jade-green silk blouse which Barbara made for me. It has big 'leg of mutton' sleeves, no collar and buttons down the front. I had it made for when I appeared in the concert at the Drury Lane theatre before Prince Charles and Princess Diana to celebrate the Falklands victory.

Then there's a bight pink silk blouse in a kind of square, deco style which Barbara sent over from England to New York for me. I've got quite a collection of silk shirts, gathered over the years, which are very handy. I like to wear them under a T-shirt or sweater with the collar showing.

As mentioned, I've developed a taste for wearing dresses. They make me feel feminine in a very classic way. I know there is some objection to that whole idea these days, but I don't go along with the view that women should never look deliberately feminine. I've got a successful career; I'm a mother; I know I can cope with my own life, and if I enjoy looking feminine in addition to this I can't see the harm.

(Opposite) **Feeling very relaxed and pensive in my blue checked shirt.**

There are a number of dresses I've bought for special occasions. Perhaps the one which amuses me most – because it seems so improbable – is my little black cocktail dress by Calvin Klein. I decided that for a particular occasion I had been invited to, I ought to wear the classic little black dress. It's in fact a very good basic – something most people find useful at times – so if you see a good little black dress and can afford it, I would suggest buying it there and then. That's far better than looking frantically for something when the occasion suddenly demands a formal dress. It took me a while to find mine. I scavenged around the shops wondering if I would ever find anything suitable. Eventually I found this rather demure little number in black velvet, but I do feel very dressy in it.

Gorgeous materials are worth buying when you see them. If you have a dressmaker or can manage even just a simple bit of dressmaking yourself, it's possible to make up a simple shift in, say, a wonderful piece of textured and patterned cloth, and it will look sensational. Many people feel that a lovely garment needs intricate cut and design, but while this may be true of a very stark, plain fabric, it just isn't true of rich material. A friend used an exquisite piece of dark blue brocade, embroidered with gold peacock feathers, to make a very simple, pleated skirt and jerkin top. And it looked marvellous.

One of Barbara Hulanicki's little black numbers in gorgeous shiny material; will make anyone feel just a little sinful.

(Opposite) **Just the opposite mood. A sexy pink leather two-piece that shouts glamour time!**

Most of us have one or two favourite garments – they become like old friends – and mine are the ones Barbara Hulanicki made me for my appearance on the Michael Parkinson TV show in Britain and for when I starred in *Cinderella* in the West End, some years ago. Then, I hadn't been singing long and Barbara quite rightly gauged that I needed something to give me confidence. She created this amazing butterfly dress in white and pink, which moved as I did. That was a dress we talked through all the way. On this occasion, Barbara had firm ideas as to how it should look. Barbara makes me laugh because she says I nearly always end up in fuchsia – it's true that's a colour I really love as I feel it gives a glow to my colouring.

Barbara also made me a very special outfit when I was asked to sing in the Butterfly Ball at the Albert Hall, another dress full of life and movement, but it rather put in the shade the other performers who had been decked out in old-fashioned crinolines from a theatrical costumier's.

Something I've learned during my years as a model and working in show business, is how to put together quick-change outfits. Layering is the basis, but it's also a question of understanding what will go on fast and look good when it's been put on that way. Leotards are wonderful because they can be used as a slinky top to a skirt and then you can always throw a big embroidered shawl around the shoulders to give a kind of exotic, gypsy effect. A leotard works well, too, as the undergarment with trousers and a cardigan jacket. If you have a long-sleeved leotard you can wear a pretty waistcoat over the top, and perhaps a pair of shorts with socks and sneakers. These are just a few ideas, and the lovely thing with leotards is it's so easy to be inventive. I have built up quite a selection of leotards because of course they don't wear out quickly. And although there are some beautiful, expensive ones in the shops, it is possible to buy them quite cheaply from most department stores.

In contrast to leotards, I have a selection of suits. I don't wear them regularly but sometimes I love the sharp, elegant look they give. That's an image it can be fun to project sometimes. I believe that most women look good in suits, but there are different types for different body shapes. The very sleek Zoot Suit style with sharp, pronounced lapels, for example, looks best on tall, slim people, whereas the beautifully cut, classic jackets like riding jackets with straight skirts, or very simple Chanel-type suits, look good on shorter people and those with broader hips.

One of my particular favourites is a man's suit by Perry Ellis, a leading American designer. It's got baggy trousers and as an alternative, a skirt. The jacket is very tailored and elegant. A good suit is a classic garment which will always look beautiful. Suits are an item which go beyond fashion. They have an identity and a life of their own. I do think it's worth investing in a good one, in something like a worsted wool or cotton and silk. Of course, it is possible to buy cheaper versions, but they rarely keep their line and look so well. It is worth hunting for suits in sales – it's remarkable the cuts in price you can find. At sale-time I would go to one of the very smart shops which stock top quality clothing to look for your suit. I have a friend who went to Burberry in London during a sale and found a beautiful, soft-grey suit with a revered jacket and a very well cut, straight skirt for one-third of its original price.

throw out a coat and I am particularly fond now of the ones which date back several years. There is the printed Ossie Clark long coat which I didn't wear for about ten years and then I dug it out for an occasion and suddenly everyone was asking where they could get one. Such is the power of looking original because, of course, that long straight style of coat which was so popular in the Sixties, just doesn't exist now.

I have an amazing fake leopardskin, also from years back. I think it looks gloriously eccentric. I'm delighted I hung on to it and I do advise anyone with a garment which quite clearly isn't likely to be repeated, to give it wardrobe space.

Now I wouldn't buy a real fur coat, certainly not one from an endangered species. Why endanger beautiful creatures when there are masses of other beautiful fabrics and skins on the market which don't affect the future of animals?

What I do have is a sheepskin coat which I bought on impulse, and it's probably the most expensive thing I've ever bought. It's a pastel peach- and pink-coloured, full-length coat with big 'leg o' mutton' sleeves in a Borgia shape by the Italian designer Fendi. I saw it in a shop window and had to buy it.

The only kind of fur that's fun.

Not that such impulses always work. I once saw an amazing leather coat. It was the most beautiful thing I had seen, and I thought that, as I was earning money doing a Broadway show, it was reasonable to treat myself. I rushed into the shop, tried it on, and there in the mirror was this apparition. I looked hideous. It was a real lesson because, having modelled so many different things, I tend to assume that most clothes will work on me – but this just didn't.

I had a similar experience when Japanese fashions were all the rage. I like the very big, blown-out looking coats, and I thought I'd try getting one of them. I found one I really liked, tried it on and – do you know? I looked exactly like a Smurf! My little head was sticking out like a pin and I was totally swamped. I had to forget being fashionable during that phase – the Japanese look wasn't for me!

My most daring buy is a little black leather skirt which clings so tightly I can hardly walk. It's a bit absurd and madly tarty – but that's the fun of such a garment, isn't it? Who wants a well-cut, sensible, black leather skirt that looks like something off the golf course?

My Style of Footwear

Someone once described me as having a fetish for shoes! Well, I'm not sure about that . . . but certainly I am a compulsive buyer of shoes and boots. Don't ask me why, I haven't got around to analysing it. But by keeping just about every pair I've bought in the past couple of decades, I have well over 100 pairs. I sometimes think I could wear paper bags more easily than give up my boots and shoes!

Certainly footwear makes a huge difference to the way you look in clothes. I love high heels and have several pairs of very classic, plain leather court shoes with high heels, in different colours, which I wear with dresses and suits – or I might wear them with tight pants if I felt like a sexy look!

I don't have many flat shoes, but these are a good basic buy and plain, ballet-style pumps can be bought in many shops. They go well with tight trousers and leggings as well as with long loose dresses and skirts, or with very short skirts or shorts. If you don't want to spend much on simple shoes like these, it is worth searching for a fabric pair. Many of the big chain stores do up-to-the-minute styles in fabric.

In my view boots are lovely with most clothes. I particularly like the canvas and cotton ankle boots which have been around for a few summers. They look good with short skirts and cut-off

I'm never legless, just sometimes bodyless!

Putting the boot in.

trousers. And of course a pair of plain leather boots will team well with most clothes and will last for many years. I do like the soft, roll-down boots with jeans, and in second-hand shops you sometimes find the old-fashioned, pirate-style boots – I have a pair – from years back. They look good with tight jeans.

I keep all my boots because it is surprising how often an outfit needs footwear which tones in precisely. I have boots in quite a lot of different colours. One way, of course, of getting footwear to tone in, if you don't have the right shade, is to apply a home-dye. There is a very good range of colours these days, and it isn't difficult.

I would never sacrifice comfort for style. I feel it's very important to have shoes and boots which you can walk in comfortably. No point in getting corns and blisters just because a particular pair of shoes looks stylish. In fact, Barbara Hulanicki has a go at me sometimes because I insist on wearing 'old favourites' with lavish new dresses when I know I'm going to be on my feet for a while. When I performed in the London West End show of *Captain Beaky* I wore my marvellous new dress with an old pair of Biba boots underneath. There's something reassuring about a pair of boots which are like old friends. And they gave me that extra bit of confidence.

I also have some pairs of very old shoes. A friend sent me a wonderful pair of soft, kid shoes, which are probably from the 1940s. I love some of these beautifully made, old shoes, and if you look in shops selling old clothes, it is quite often possible to pick up a pair of really pretty shoes cheaply.

Some rarities I just couldn't bear to part with.

PUTTING TOGETHER DIFFERENT LOOKS

I REALIZE that I do have a bigger collection of clothes than most people – well that's not surprising with the modelling and theatrical work I've done – but the point is they are a mixed bag of things and it really isn't necessary to have a large collection in order to put together stylish looks.

The essence of style is the ability to put together clothes in an imaginative and interesting way. Mix and match collections are often excellent, although sometimes too they can be dull and a bit limited. And while it is useful to be able to buy all the bits a designer has planned to go together, remember that you can also take the bits apart and use them quite differently. It is amazing, for example, how different the effect of a simple, long-sleeved T-shirt can be if worn with jeans and a scarf knotted jauntily around the neck for a very casual look. Team it with a full, flouncy skirt, tucked in and belted with a broad cummerbund, then add lots of beads at the neck, and perhaps a little waistcoat over the top, and you achieve a far smarter and dressier look – the simplicity of the T-shirt actually makes for elegance.

It's curious but there tends to be a strong feeling of morality with fashion as though mixing up different designers' clothes is somehow wrong. I think we've all been a bit brainwashed with the idea of 'getting it right' as though there was such a thing. If you have bought yourself a garment or collection of garments, then they are yours to use as you wish. For example, if you like the utility look, you could buy a couple of pairs of loose, crumpled cotton pants with lots of zips and pockets, a big, strong-looking T-shirt, a full-cut jacket. Add some very skimpy T-shirts, big cummerbunds, neck scarves, loose heavy belts with big buckles, and mix them in all sorts of different ways. This may sound like a lot of items, but I don't necessarily mean you to go out and buy them all new. You may already have some in your wardrobe, in which case bring them out and use them again. Otherwise, if you have a sewing machine, it is possible to make simple T-shirts. Cummerbunds can be made from a length of fabric hand-stitched around the edge, and so can neck scarves. And it is possible to buy things like old men's vests in wonderful natural cotton or wool mix from utility stores and old clothing shops. Try those places which get in job-lots of men's clothing; the clothes here are not considered to be valuable or 'antique' like so many women's items now are, and are consequently at rock bottom prices.

One idea is to wear the pants, the big T-shirt and a heavy belt slung around the hips, with perhaps canvas boots and a scarf – one of those embroidered North African scarves that look a bit like a drying-up cloth and sell in many of the ethnic shops which stock Indian ware. Worn rolled around the collar looks good. Another idea is to wear the pants, a skimpy T-shirt and a big, bold cummerbund, to create a quite different, swashbuckling effect.

If you have have in your summer wardrobe, as I do, soft-cut, flowery skirts reaching to below the knee, you can create a very gentle, peasanty look by wearing espadrilles, a strappy T-shirt and lots of big bangles. A scarf wrapped like a big bandeau around the head also looks good. Or for a completely different effect, wear the skirt with a very tailored linen jacket, a collarless blouse and flat pump shoes.

For several seasons retailers, magazines, and fashion writers have been putting forward a very hard, utilitarian look – tough cotton trousers worn with big, loose jackets, parachute suits – and the way it is presented is generally as a total look. But try taking the look apart, use just the jacket, cut large with big shoulders, and team it with a straight skirt and fine-knit v-neck sweater; worn with a fine chain necklace, you have a delightful mix of the masculine and the feminine. Or you could take a pair of utility pants and wear them with a tailored, flannel jacket with the collar turned up, and a white lace camisole underneath. Purists might shriek in horror at the idea, but actually the effect would be stunning.

Styles to Suit Different Sizes

The point about devising your own style is, as I've said before, making it suit your body. I have a friend who is not very tall and quite plump, and she agonizes a good deal about what to wear. But when she began to 'invent' fashion, she started enjoying clothes far more. For instance, she wears Indian trousers with a drawstring waist in a lovely mauve fabric with a silver thread; she tops these with a big, loose T-shirt and over that she wears a battered leather waistcoat bought from a charity shop. The look is terrific.

Another idea from a plump friend is to go for the kind of clothes which create a sense of slimness – plain-coloured dresses cut in a fairly simple or straight shape, or trousers which are dark and do not cling too tightly, and then add outrageous or very bold detail where it will not emphasize size. For example, this friend has a straight, dark-blue cotton dress. It's very simple with a high neck, short sleeves and a tubular skirt. By itself it is remarkable only for its dullness, but she ties a very big, patterned scarf around the hips, then adds a couple of loose belts over the top. And although she has quite large hips, the effect is not at all enlarging, it just gives a sense of fun to the outfit. Sometimes she wears the scarf, like a shawl, over her shoulders and goes in for very elaborate shoes in order to divert attention from her overall shape.

If you are larger than average or shorter than average, don't be put off from trying a fashionable and daring look. If you are large, the cardinal rule is to buy things large enough; no-one was ever made to look slimmer by wearing skin-tight clothes. Also, it's not a good idea to cover a large body in shocking-pink or pastel colours, because they do create an illusion of size. But that doesn't mean you must bury yourself in dingy, 'disguising' shades. I know plenty of large people who wear vivid jade, purple, scarlet, electric blue, and look wonderful. These colours may be eye-catching but they are not enlarging.

It is generally sensible to wear shoes with some heel, to give added height which detracts from the sense of size – although avoid stilettos or very high heels. They are appallingly bad for the back and, far from making a large person look tall and elegant, they usually make her look ungainly and unbalanced. Wear low-heel slingbacks, sandals, court shoes, or well-cut, plain-coloured pumps.

It isn't wise to cut a large body in half with a broad belt, but do wear narrow belts (not too tight!) either around the waist or slung around the hips. And jewellery is an asset to the large. Bold ear-rings, bangles and necklaces which do not engulf the neck, provided they are not too enormous and garish, distract the eye from the body.

There is so much emphasis on being slim these days that we tend to think it is only the larger person who has a problem. In fact, of course, small people also worry about how they look. And with so many of today's fashions being designed for the willowy woman, that's understandable. If you are short it is sensible to aim for clothes which are not going to look too big. For example, a tailored suit made for someone of about five foot eight will probably never look very good on a person five inches shorter. The proportions will be wrong, and no amount of altering will change that.

But the baggy, large-cut, sporty clothes can be worn by someone small. I have a friend of about five foot who bought big loose trousers, a large jacket and a strong leather belt. She wore the trousers with a small T-shirt, and belted them in so that the fabric came over the top of the belt. She then rolled up the legs to mid-calf and rolled the sleeves of the jacket to mid-arm. She looked very comfortable, colourful and casual.

It is of course more difficult if you want to buy a skirt or dress which is too long and a bit broad on the shoulder or the waist. If it is a casual style, like a shirtwaister, the problem can be overcome. A shirtwaister dress with overlarge shoulders looks quite nice if the waist is nipped in with a large belt, and then probably only the hem will need taking up. For more tailored dresses you really need to be a competent dressmaker to do alterations.

Another very small friend has the best idea of all. She goes to the children's departments of big stores and buys some stunning clothes, much cheaper than in the fashion departments. In Britain, no tax is charged on children's clothes so it makes good sense, and frankly, teenagers' clothes are very fashionable, and also quite large – I gather that each new generation is larger than the last – so anyone under about five-foot-three could probably find some good buys there. (Tax on children's clothes in the USA varies from State to State, so check before shopping there.)

Small people, provided they are not very overweight, can get away with lots of lovely patterned prints and mixed colours – although avoid very large designs as these tend to make the person inside look lost.

Tall people also worry about how they look in clothes – as well as where to buy them. In London, there is an excellent shop called Long Tall Sally which has clothes specially made for particularly tall people and they are very aware of the latest looks. Otherwise you will have to hunt for clothes with generous hems. I have a friend who seeks out the shops which stock homespun clothes because they generally go in for mid-calf, full skirts. She then wears these skirts on the knee, perhaps with a tailored blouse, and the effect is very chic. She also has a couple of wonderful Austrian dirndl skirts which have lasted through several winters.

For the tall, the clothing warehouses which stock men's and women's working clothes tend to be invaluable. Work clothes are generally cut much larger than ordinary fashion items, and while some are hideous I have seen people in lovely boiler suits and dungarees, as well as collarless shirts and cotton drill trousers bought from such places. There are also shops like Flip, the old American clothes chain of shops, which opened recently in London. If you don't find clothes which are long enough among the women's garments in these places, then you might well among the small-sized men's items.

I have found that, in America, it is much easier to shop for clothes to fit tall women as most designers there cater for them. There is also a chain of shops called Shelly's Tall Girls with about sixty branches.

Tall people tend to look best in clothes which divide them up. The long straight dress which slims the large person, makes the tall look like an asparagus stick. I know one woman who is six foot, and wears very fluffy, large knitwear, usually with some bold design or motif. She always wears loose baggy trousers – tight ones make you look still taller – and generally she wears tall, bright-coloured boots. Full-skirted dresses belted at the waist look good, and trousers worn at mid-calf tend to detract from height.

Of course, why not just enjoy being tall? Fashion and the stylish looks around are often geared to the tall person. Standing erect, wearing wonderfully bold prints, beautifully cut clothes, outfits with lots of detail and layers, is the key to looking stylish.

Another intricate detailed Hulanicki outfit that needs careful timing and perfect accessories, and is a wow.

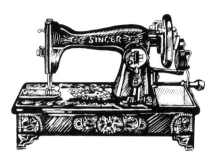

A MARVELLOUS alternative to buying clothes is, of course, to make your own. I've always enjoyed sewing, although I get less and less time to do it these days. Recently I did find time though to make an actor friend two tailored shirts for Christmas when we were working together in New York, and I made Hallowe'en outfits for us both to wear to a party. I was a cat and he was a mouse. That was great fun and came about in fact because he gave me a sewing machine as a present – I had been moaning that mine was left behind in England.

When I was younger I always made my own clothes, and became quite good at it. That doesn't mean I have a special talent, it's just a matter of practice. By making your own clothes you can be sure of getting exactly the garment you want, for too often when you go out to buy you find an outfit which is nearly right, but not quite. Once you have gained some experience at dressmaking you will be able to create your own patterns, or at least adapt a bought one.

A sewing machine is essential. Sewing a full-scale garment by hand is no fun, although little finicky seams and hems can be sewn by hand. There are obvious advantages to an electric machine or, better still, get one of the new electronic ones which are very fast, quiet and accurate. They do a lot of work in the minimum amount of time, and many will embroider, hem, overstitch, and button-hole. They've become very sophisticated. On the other hand, an old-fashioned treadle or manual machine also works well – in fact there have been plenty of occasions when I thought one would be better. It's too easy for a very fast machine to run too far and then you have to spend time unpicking; a slower machine is much easier to control.

The other essential is to leave yourself enough time. Many people embark upon things at the last minute and find themselves panicking because the seams won't go straight, the cut is wrong and so on. I've done it myself, trying frantically to finish a garment in time for a special occasion, and more often than not it's been a disaster. Here are a few basic tips before you start:

1 *Choose a pattern you will be able to follow.* It's too easy to be dazzled by the elaborate designer patterns which companies such as Vogue offer. Once you are a proficient dressmaker it's wonderful to be able to conjure up a Calvin Klein original, or whatever, but to start with it is sensible to choose a really simple-style garment with basically straight lines and not much detail.

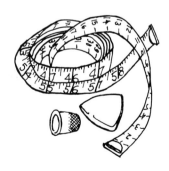

Most of the big pattern companies do easy-to-sew lines and some very nice designs are available.

2 *Make sure the pattern is your size.* Few people conform absolutely to the manufacturer's sizes and whereas you can't do much about this with a bought garment, with one you make yourself it is possible to have a perfect fit. The correct measurements are therefore all important. So strip down to the underwear you would wear with the garment. Wear shoes too – leaving them off may give you a wrong idea of the length and look of the garment you want. Now, first measure your bust, placing the tape over the fullest part. Don't let it slip down at the back. Then measure your chest under the arms, around the body and under the bust. Measure your waist by resting the tape on the smallest part of it and pulling the tape taut but not tight. Don't breathe in or attempt to look slim at this moment – it may well mean that you end up with a garment as tight as a skin. The hips have to be measured at the top and bottom as both areas may not be the same. The top should be measured three to four inches below the waist, the bottom seven to eight inches below. Measure for length from the back of the neck to the waist and from the front of the neck, between the breasts, at the front. Measure for length at the front and back from the the middle of the waist. (It may be better, however, to leave the length until the garment is made up.) Then put these measurements on to the pattern and see if they are the same. If there is a very small difference, it is probably worth leaving but if you have, say, an inch discrepancy, draw an inch extra beside the seam markings.

3 *Choose the right fabric.* If you are a beginner, it is wise to use fabric which does not move around or stretch much. Easy fabrics are gaberdine, cotton, denim, poplin and sailcloth; for a winter garment, try wool gabardine, worsted wool, flannel and plain wool. Fabrics which are difficult to control are velvet, soft, fine cloths such as silk and jersey, and fabrics with a very loose weave. It is also wise to avoid fabrics with large, pronounced patterns as it can be difficult to match the design at the seam edges. It's better to go for a pattern of tiny scattered flowers, or a small design where it won't matter if the pattern doesn't meet up, rather than a huge chintzy rose or a pictorial print. If you are using a loose weave cotton, an Indian cotton, or any fabric which might shrink, it is sensible to wash and iron the cloth before beginning. Nothing is more maddening than making a garment, then finding it would fit only a child after the first wash. Stretch fabrics should be laid out flat and left to 'relax' overnight. Lining gives a garment body and is particularly recommended for loose-

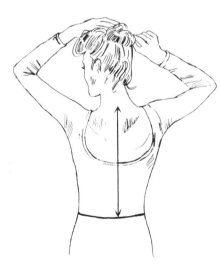

weave fabric. It is also worth pressing the garment as you go along. This avoids wrinkly seams because the fabric was creased, and mistakes with the markings.

4 *Have everything ready before you begin.* You will need a sharp pair of dressmaking scissors and a small pair for cutting off threads. Have out tacking thread and – most important – the right thread for the garment. It's not a good idea, for example, to try to sew crêpe de Chine with heavy-gauge cotton thread, or heavy cotton with the finest thread. The patterns tell you on the back what to use. Have the sewing machine threaded up before you begin and be sure you have enough thread: it's unfuriating to find you need to rush out to the shops mid-way through your creativity. Have ready tailor's chalk for marking and pins for pinning. Also a pincushion, which I find surprisingly useful for sticking pins in when you are doing three things at once, or removing them while machining.

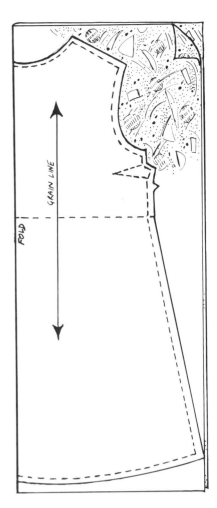

5 *Lay out the fabric on a large table or work surface and place all the pieces of pattern on to it.* Fold the fabric where necessary for the pieces of pattern that need to be cut double. Once your pattern is carefully laid out and you are certain half is not going with the weave and half against, or the whole thing is not being cut across the bias, you are ready to pin down and do the markings. Patterns have very clear instructions as to what needs marking, and this you do with tacking thread or tailor's chalk. Cut the seam notches as marked and then remove the pattern from the fabric. Tack up your garment to ensure the seams are straight, and that collars and sleeves are sitting right. Try it on and make any alterations you wish before it is irrevocably stitched.

6 *Your garment is now ready to be sewn up.* Machine the main seams first, then – very carefully – the smaller ones. You may find it worth doing tricky bits by hand. When you have finished, turn the garment inside out, snip off all the loose cotton ends and with pinking shears cut the edges of any seams which may need it. If you have a machine which overlocks, it is well worth using this to overstitch seams.

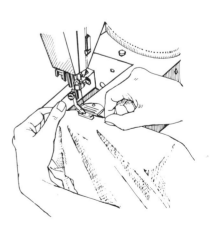

Apart from making whole garments, you can of course 'tart up' a ready-made garment. Buy an old lace collar in a market and stitch it to a jumper or dress. Chop up an old blouse and turn it into a T-shirt by removing the sleeves, cutting the neck low and making it slim-line. Always, before discarding garments which have become unfashionable, try adapting them. It is surprising how the look of a garment can be completely changed just through a few alterations.

41

SKIN CARE

CARING for my skin has become a habit. Like most people, there are times when I feel I really cannot be bothered to clean off my make-up or give my face the necessary treatments, but I am tough with myself because I know the damage that can be caused to the skin through neglect.

Already, I am trying to teach Carly the importance of proper skin care. She gets very grubby at times – and there's nothing wrong in that of course – and she has fun doing it. But instead of just nagging her to clean her face, I try to point out that facial cleanliness is not only to do with appearance but is also to do with keeping her skin in good condition.

How wonderful to have perfect skin, like in one of those advertisements (presumably shot with loads of make-up and good lighting) which make grown women appear to have baby-soft skin. But that's not being realistic. As we age, our skin becomes coarse, and lines and wrinkles develop – this applies to mine as much as anyone's. However, don't object to these inevitable signposts of life; instead, care for your skin and try to make it look as good as possible for the stage it is at.

If you want to look attractive and healthy, you should treat your skin properly. I'm not a fanatic: I don't have time for the kind of person who gets very upset if she finds a tiny spot or blemish – and I have known people, particularly in the modelling world, who really do go into a full-scale depression at the sight of a pimple – but when you are on public display a lot, as I am, it is important to look as attractive and fresh as possible.

Caring for your skin doesn't guarantee you will never have a blemish. I know if I am under stress, a bit overtired, or if I have just been out enjoying myself too much, I get the odd spot, and my skin begins to look quite dowdy. No amount of treatment and creams will change that until I sort out the cause. But aside from that, a rigid, regular skin-care routine does keep me looking better than if I ignore my skin or forget to moisturize it for a couple of days. I know, because I've tried both ways!

There are particular times of the day when, almost in auto-drive, I deal with my skin. When I get up in the morning, I shower, then apply cream to my whole body and follow this by cleansing my face and applying my day cream. It's the same in the evening. No matter what time I come in, I always cleanse and moisturize my face. Sometimes when I'm absolutely exhausted after a day of two shows – when even picking up a piece of cotton-wool feels like too much effort – I think I'll let myself off the hook. But luckily, I have a really cussed conscience which gives me a good kick and I just get on and do it. Which is just as well because if you slip once, it tends to happen again . . . and then again.

I have dry skin which has the advantage of not getting spotty or shiny-looking, but it does require a lot of moisturizing; in winter particularly, I am aware of how dry it feels. Then I tend to use a very rich moisturizer and apply it frequently. Oily skins, of course, are prone to develop spots, but they are a bonus in the tough winter winds or in warm sunshine when the atmosphere dries skins like mine almost to parchment texture.

It is important to know your skin type and to treat it accordingly. There are products these days to deal with every different type of skin, so it should be possible to find something which works well for you.

STRUCTURE OF THE SKIN

THE skin is a bit like an elaborate sandwich. On the top is the layer of epidermis, in the middle is the dermis, and at the bottom is the hypodermis.

The epidermis is just a coating of dead cells, stacked together to form the complexion as we see it. It may not sound so appetizing but in fact these dead cells are very useful because they provide a protective wall against bacteria. Underneath this are young cells pushing to get through, which make me think of children determined to do as they want, obstinately disregarding any adult who gets in the way! When you have a defoliation treatment, which strips off a layer of dead cells, it actually stimulates the production of the new cells. But then as soon as these new cells are exposed to the elements they, too, begin to age.

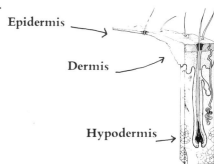

Epidermis

Dermis

Hypodermis

The middle layers of the 'sandwich' is the dermis. This is made up of connective tissues, and it is here that 'parcels' of collagen (the substance which, with two per cent of elastin, causes the skin's elasticity) are found. Here, too, are the nerves, blood and the sweat glands which produced sebum, a very useful oily substance which stays on the surface of the skin, helping to keep moisture in and bacteria out. The dermis is a bit like a woven fabric in texture, and it is through this area of the skin that you feel heat, pressure, cold and pain.

At the bottom of all this is the hypodermis, a layer of fatty tissue which acts as a kind of protective buffer between the skin and the rest of the body.

Because most articles and books on skin care deal only with the complexion or the outer skin, we tend to forget what a fascinating and intricate material the skin is. Underneath the outer layer of skin we have a kind of salt lake which surrounds and feeds the cells; this acts as a dumping ground for the cells' waste matter, and is most important because if the cells didn't have a 'dump' for their waste and were unable to deposit it, we would become ill.

1 DRY SKIN   Generally fine-textured, dry skin may feel taut at times, which is usually a sign that it needs moisturizing. It may occasionally become flaky, and is sensitive to extremes of temperature, to harsh winds or a very humid and dry atmosphere. You will probably find you need a rich day cream as well as a night time emollient. The advantage to dry skin is that it tends not to suffer from spots or blackheads, and often has a clear, matt surface.

But with dry skin, wrinkles and lines form easily, so it is worth investing in a rich cream which really does moisturize well and which leaves the skin feeling comfortable. There are no miracle cures for lines and wrinkles once they are there. The area under the eyes, where the tissue is very delicate, and the soft throat skin are particularly vulnerable.

2 GREASY SKIN   Greasy skin is often rather shiny and has a coarser texture than dry skin. It also has a tendency to form blackheads and pimples. This is most common during teenage years which, of course, is unfortunate because it is the time when most of us are very conscious and uncertain of our appearance. But at least the problem really does diminish with age. And these days there are preparations which do seem to help a good many people.

The virtue of greasy skin becomes apparent as you grow older. Where the dry-skinned person is doing battle with lines and wrinkles, greasy skins tends to stay smooth and unlined far longer. And oily skins have an advantage in the sun too – they tend to tan easily and painlessly.

3 COMBINATION SKIN   Someone with this kind of skin generally has dry cheeks but an oily patch down the centre of the face, along the forehead, nose and chin. This is a very common skin type and it is possible you may need to follow two skin regimes. Certainly, it is sensible to apply a rich moisturizer to the cheeks, and something suitable for an oily skin along the centre panel.

4 NORMAL SKIN   Even normal skin requires regular treatment if you are to keep it looking its best. I suggest cleansing and toning your face as for dry skin and then applying a slightly lighter moisturizer. Regular moisturizing is all-important to maintain a smooth complexion.

Knowing your skin type helps you to identify the kind of products you should use. I am a great believer, too, in understanding how skin comes to be the way it is because it will help you to know how best to look after it.

Understanding your skin is really necessary to keep that schoolgirl complexion a bit longer.

A SIMPLE and regular routine is best for my skin. Some people seem to have an absolute army of pots and potions they use, but frankly I can't imagine what the different things do – or how people remember in which order they should be used! I find that the traditional method of cleansing, toning and moisturizing works well and, in addition, occasionally I give my face a treat with a home facial or a salon treatment.

It is important to allow yourself enough time. I set aside ten minutes morning and evening, which is ample time and really not much in the course of a day to devote to caring for something as precious as skin.

My Face-care Routine

1 *Cleanse*   Cleanse the skin thoroughly twice a day. In the morning, cleansing removes any dust or grime which may have got on to your face during the night. (After all, when you have moisturizer on the skin – as presumably you do at night – dust can stick easily.) Cleansing at night will remove any of the day's dirt and grime which has gathered. If you wear make-up, this *must* be removed of course. Make-up – if it is left on while you sleep – can clog the pores, prevent the skin breathing and lead to spots and blemishes.

Creams and lotions are very effective cleansing agents. They combine with the make-up or dirt on the face and act to lift it off the skin. If you use a cleansing cream or lotion you will probably need two applications to get the skin really clean, and if you wear much make-up, you may well find three applications are necessary. The idea is for the cotton-wool – the most effective substance for removing cleanser – eventually to be absolutely clean when you wipe it over the face. Cleansers should be rubbed on to the face gently but firmly enough to penetrate into the skin. Leave on for a few seconds, then wipe cotton-wool over the complexion, drawing up the cleanser and dirt.

Some people prefer washing the face to cleansing it, either every time or interspersed with dry cleansing. There has been much debate about whether or not soap and water are good for the skin, with some 'experts' arguing that they are excellent while others say they are disastrous. It really is difficult to know what to think. But from the talking and reading I have done, I have come to the conclusion that there are no hard and fast rules. It is something that only you and your skin can work out – by trial and error.

If you have greasy skin, you may like the feeling a soap and water wash gives but it is important not to use a very harsh soap.

Many soaps which have been recommended for oily skins are acidic and made of harsh detergents which, far from being helpful, can damage the chemical structure of the cells on the epidermis – the very cells which work to provide protection for the surface of the skin. If you have a dry skin, it's important to choose a soap which will not dry it out still more. Even some gentle soaps, made from fats, may cause dryness because they have been processed with caustic soda. You may not be able to find out just which soaps fall into this category, but it is generally safe to use the plain white, super-fatted or the pH-balanced soaps. And while I don't believe in paying huge sums of money for my cosmetics, I advise you not to economize on the soap you use on your face. Many of the very cheap soaps are harsh and can upset the natural acid balance of the skin. The glycerine or oatmeal soaps sold in places like The Body Shop are best.

Another idea is to avoid soap altogether and to go for a washing cream, washing grains or a facial scrub. My beautician Christiana, in New York, made up a lovely wash from wheat and honey which I use to rub on my face, then rinse off. It leaves my skin feeling very smooth and not at all dry.

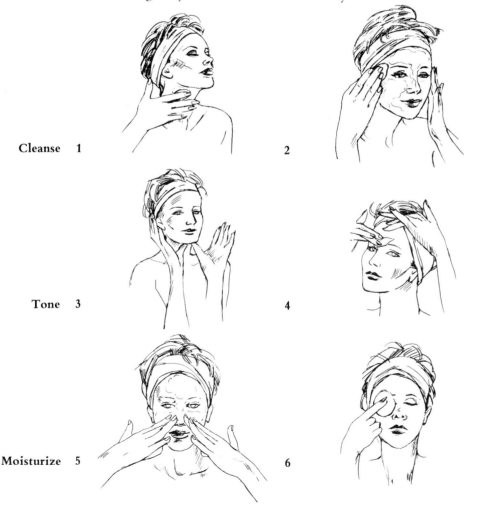

Cleanse 1   2

Tone 3   4

Moisturize 5   6

When washing your face, apply whatever substance you decide to use with the fingertips and rub in gently with a massaging motion. Leave for a few seconds, then rinse off with warm, but not hot, water. Hot water can break the capillaries and will dry out the skin. Make sure you remove all the soap or cleanser before drying your face thoroughly.

2 *Tone*   Toners are used to remove the last vestiges of make-up after you have cleansed the face, and they will leave the skin feeling pleasantly cool. For a long time astringents were recommended to remove any greasiness left by cleansers, but they are not necessary nowadays as cleansers are far less greasy. And a number of astringents contain quite a lot of alcohol which can dry the skin and obviously, if you have a dry skin like mine, that is the last thing you want.

I like to use what is generally called a skin freshener. This is often a mixture like honey and witch-hazel or flower water, and Christiana mixes for me delicious-smelling fresheners with fruit extracts – one of my favourites is strawberry! As this is a bit extravagant, and strawberries aren't available all the year round, I'll give you two recipes for making your own toner which both use ingredients you should have no trouble finding at any time. They both come from Clare Maxwell-Hudson's *Your Health and Beauty Book*.

Skin Tonic

Vinegar skin tonic:

Dilute one part of vinegar to eight parts of water. This can be used as a skin toner, in the bath or as a final rinse when washing your hair. If, however, you don't like the smell of vinegar, disguise it by mixing the following in a bottle with the vinegar: 2 tablespoons of lavender, 1 tablespoon of tarragon, ½ teaspoon of cloves and 1 tablespoon of rose petals. Leave for two weeks, but shake the bottle daily. Then strain the vinegar mixture and dilute it with the water.

It smells wonderful and is a very pretty colour.

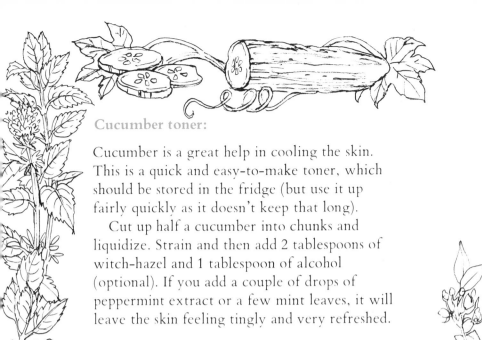

Cucumber toner:

Cucumber is a great help in cooling the skin. This is a quick and easy-to-make toner, which should be stored in the fridge (but use it up fairly quickly as it doesn't keep that long).

Cut up half a cucumber into chunks and liquidize. Strain and then add 2 tablespoons of witch-hazel and 1 tablespoon of alcohol (optional). If you add a couple of drops of peppermint extract or a few mint leaves, it will leave the skin feeling tingly and very refreshed.

Skin Toner

If your skin is very greasy with a tendency to spots, an astringent with alcohol may be worth trying, but if you find it doesn't help then use an alcohol-free freshener, as I do, which is less harsh on the skin.

Shops which sell herbal and natural cosmetics tend to stock mild fresheners which stimulate the skin slightly but do not dry it. I once tried a honey and water toner which I liked very much. Honey acts as an astringent and moisturizer at the same time – odd though that sounds – and the one I used contained oil of cloves, an antiseptic, and orange flower water.

Apply your toner liberally with a pad of cotton-wool which you wipe gently over the face and neck. The skin will feel stimulated, clean and clear, ready for moisturizing.

3 *Moisturize* When you see the enormous assortment of moisturizers available these days, and when you hear the elaborate claims made for each of them, it becomes very hard to know which to choose. So it is sensible to understand that, although some of the highly developed creams and lotions have formulas which make them easy to absorb or ingredients which temporarily make the skin look smoother, basically all moisturizers have much the same function, i.e. to prevent moisture escaping from the skin. Moisturizers create a thin film of protective coating over the skin surface which prevents the moisture getting out and also prevents dirt and make-up getting in.

The skin around the eyes is particularly delicate.

Remember to moisturize your lips as well.

The skin contains a lot of moisture, and it is moisture-loss which causes the dried-out look. Babies have about eighty per cent moisture in their skin – that is what causes their wonderful, soft, puffy look – while adults generally have about half that amount.

Moisturizers are a combination of water and oil or grease, and no matter what grandiose claims manufacturers make, that is fundamentally what you are buying. The quantities of either vary according to the formula of the product. Water-in-oil formulas, as the words suggest, are richer and contain more moisturizing ingredients than the lighter oil-in-water products. The oil-in-water kind may not be rich enough to provide the coating to hold in the skin's moisture, so you are advised to buy the richer formula if you have a very dry skin, even though it may cost a bit more.

You will need two moisturizers: a light product, perhaps a lotion, which will go under make-up and not leave your skin feeling sticky so that the make-up becomes smudged or streaky, and then at night you will need to apply something richer. Many of us, once we have found a product we like, tend to stick to it, blaming the atmosphere, the weather, our health and so on if it no longer seems to work as well as when we first used it. When this happens, it is clearly a sign that it's time for a change. For many years I washed my skin and then applied just Astral cream to it, and it was fine. But now that I am in my thirties and exposed to a lot of harsh lights when performing on stage, my skin needs something a little richer and with a more easily-absorbable texture. I still use Astral, because I find it excellent, but I am aware that it alone is not enough. It is important that, as you age, you recognize that your skin will need a richer, more active moisturizer.

Skin can also grow accustomed to products and after a while need a change: you may have been quite happy using the same product for years and then suddenly find it doesn't seem so effective any more, and the solution is simply to try a new product.

People with dry skin will naturally go for a rich product. If you have an oily skin, it is a good idea to try a non-greasy cream or lotion. With a combination skin you will probably want a rich moisturizer for the dry parts and something lighter for the greasy parts.

Eye creams have become very popular in recent years. They are specially made to a very light formula and should be applied carefully. Don't rub a rich, heavy cream around the delicate eye tissue. I have several friends who use eye creams and they are quite convinced that they have eased lines which gather around the eyes.

Remember though that skin products are big business these days. Everyone seems to be searching for a lotion or potion which really will stop the ageing process and reduce the lines, crows' feet, wrinkles and crinkles which come as we move through the years. I'm sure it would be nice to have a cream which magically could keep us looking youthful, but I mistrust the frantic quest to avoid showing any maturity – as though being forever in one's early twenties is the ultimate goal! That is rather sad. I aim to enjoy my life, particularly as I grow older and develop new abilities and new confidence – so what if that shows in my looks?

But having said this, I do recognize that there is a big emphasis nowadays on looking young, and so manufacturers will continue their research to bring us better and better products. And certainly, the moisturizers which have been appearing on the market over recent years seem excellent. This is true of both those at the medium and top price end of the market. It is fashionable to add hormones, collagen, herbs and other extras to a basic formula. I like herbs if they give a product an appealing smell and certainly there are herbs which for centuries have been known for their healing powers, so they would seem a very good idea, particularly as they cannot do any harm. But the same may not be true of hormones. It is said that some of the creams containing hormones may make the skin look softer and fuller – at least for a while (nobody is claiming that it is permanent) – but the problem is that it is not known whether these creams may have long-term side-effects. Personally, I prefer to keep away from such products.

Moisturizers are best applied by using the fingertips to work the substance into the skin. You don't need much moisturizer – a blob the size of a one-penny piece or a dime is plenty. It should be gently massaged over the skin with circular movements, going from the inside of the face by the bridge of the nose, and working outwards. Be sure to take some up to your forehead, right to the edges of your face and then, of course, down over your neck.

Apply moisturizer each morning about twenty minutes before putting on your make-up, so that you give it time to penetrate into the skin. Otherwise, if you put make-up on immediately, you may block the moisturizer or rub it off; also, an oily face can be a difficult base for applying foundation. At night, if you do not want to sleep in your moisturizer, apply it about half an hour before going to bed. This is quite long enough for the skin to absorb all it needs, and then you can wipe off the remainder.

Although applying moisturizer twice a day is generally

considered enough, some people may find their skin needs more. For example, if you are spending a lot of time in a very dry or humid atmosphere – as I am when living in New York – your skin may feel very parched and dry just a few hours after you have moisturized it. If this is the case, give it another coat of cream or lotion. It is a good idea, too, to apply a small amount of moisturizer when you re-do make-up during the day.

In summer, when you may be splashing water on your face at intervals throughout the day, it's wise to top up with a drop of moisturizer afterwards. I have a friend who swims a lot and she finds her skin is always very dry afterwards – even if her face has not been much in the water. She always carries a tube of moisturizing cream in her swimming bag.

Keep moisturizer with you in your make-up purse, then your skin need never get unpleasantly dry. Many cosmetic houses produce a fairly basic moisturizer in small containers. Or you could buy sample tubes of creams. These are ideal because they fit into a very small bag or purse.

Allergic reactions

You may find that your skin reacts badly to particular products. Perhaps a rash will form, or you skin will feel sore or go blotchy, or it may become very dry. Should any of these occur, stop using the product and see if the condition improves.

Face products are very carefully tested these days but there will always be somebody who reacts badly to a certain ingredient which doesn't affect the rest of us. London beautician Joan Price, an expert in these matters, pointed out to me that some very basic, natural products are known irritants – so it isn't just the elaborate chemical brews which cause the trouble as nature purists tend to think. Possible irritant ingredients are: lanolin, bees' wax, cocoa butter, corn starch, rice starch, almond oil, boric acid and honey. Of course, not everyone will react badly to these, but it's worth knowing that one might be the culprit if you do get a reaction.

If you have a sensitive skin, use one of the hypo-allergenic ranges of skin-care products. Many of the leading cosmetic companies make these – indeed, it's interesting how many of the newest and best promoted creams and lotions are hypo-allergenic. Even if your skin has never reacted badly to cosmetics, it's worth considering using these as they are very gentle.

Facials

Facials are a wonderful treat. Friends sometimes ask me why I bother with them, if I look after my skin with a daily regime. The answer is that facials do a far more thorough job than a cleanser and toner can ever do; they also leave me feeling good.

It's particularly pleasant, and beneficial to the skin, to have a professional facial. I always thought that just slapping my yeast pack on the face, then rinsing it off was good enough, but since being introduced to Christiana, I have realized that there is a lot more to it. First of all, a professional will apply the mask carefully. She or he knows just how long to leave it, and will probably give your face a massage after doing so. I have learnt a lot from seeing how the professionals work and from asking them questions. So if you can afford to have a professional facial – even if it is just once every six months and then you do your own in between – it is worthwhile.

The function of a facial is to remove the dead cells on the surface of the skin. In recent years, cosmetic companies have gone in for exfoliating products – as the process of removing these cells is called – in a big way. Basically, they do what women have been doing for centuries: they act as a stripping agent for the top layer of cells. Hundreds of years ago women used pumice paste and sea sand which they rubbed in with a cloth. Now we have grainy creams, oatmeal scrubs, lotions and potions to do the job. Removing these cells helps to stimulate the rise of new cells to the surface. Facials also deep-cleanse and feed moisture into the skin, and they stimulate circulation – I am always amazed at how alive my skin feels after a treatment.

My facials at the salon last an hour, and I regard them as a time for relaxation and for letting myself go as well as being of benefit to the complexion. If you decide to invest in a professional facial, make it a real treat for yourself. Don't just lie there as you are being treated, worrying about what to make for supper or whether your boy friend has been seeing an old flame! Instead, try to relax your mind and clear it of all thoughts. Christiana always plays classical music, which I find very relaxing.

Christiana first cleanses my skin, to remove it of all traces of make-up and surface dirt. The skin is then steamed, which draws dirt out of it. You can do this yourself at home by pouring a kettle of boiling water into a bowl, then leaning over the bowl so that the steam is able to work on the face – but do be careful not to spill the hot water over you. The heat of the steam helps to draw up all skin impurities. You can also do this, although not quite as effectively, by sitting in a hot bath after cleansing the face.

After the steaming, Christiana massages my face for a quarter of an hour. This is the part I enjoy most, something I consider worth paying for. Although it's possible to give yourself a massage at home by gently moving your fingertips over the skin in a circular movement working outwards from the centre of the face, which will leave your skin feeling good and the circulation pumping well, it is not as luxurious a feeling or as relaxing as having a professional massage.

The massage is followed by a mask. Christiana uses a paraffin mask, which solidifies on the face and is then peeled off. This is an effective way of removing dead cells, and many of the gels and honey-based masks you can buy work in the same way, by forming a kind of skin over your own skin which is then lifted off when it is dry. (I don't recommend trying the paraffin mask yourself though – best left to the professionals!)

After the facial, my face is moisturized. My skin always needs to be thoroughly moisturized – although it's nowhere near as dried-out and 'hungry' as when I used clay masks. These are excellent if you have an oily skin which needs drying out, but anybody who has a dry or even normal skin, is better off using one of the gentler gels containing herbs or plant extracts which are now on the market. There are creams, too, which are good for very dry and sensitive skins. But before buying, do check which kind of mask you are getting.

A home-made mask is cheaper than the commercial variety, but do bear in mind that rubbing avocado, wheatgerm oil, or whatever, around you face can be a messy business. An appealing recipe which Christiana passed on to me is to mix the yolk of an egg with a Vitamin E capsule. It needs to be left on your face until dry, then washed off. Joan Price, in London, uses a little vegetable or nut oil mixed with a few drops of warm water and lemon juice which she applies to the face, leaves for a few minutes to dry and then gently rubs off. Face masks are fun to make at home with ingredients from the larder. Here are a couple I recommend:

Egg mask

The egg yolk contains protein and lecithin and is very nourishing while the white has astringent qualities.

For normal skin add 1 teaspoon of honey and 1 teaspoon of almond oil to a beaten egg. If your skin is dry, use only the yolk and mix it with honey and a teaspoon of wheatgerm oil. For greasy skin, use only the egg white and add a teaspoon of almond oil. Whisk up the mixture and apply it to your face. Then relax for 10–15 minutes before wiping off gently.

Avocado mask

Avocados are very nourishing and are especially
good if you have dry skin. Any avocado will do.
You don't need to buy the most perfect-looking
pears – black, bruised ones will do just as well
and will be a lot cheaper!
Mash and sieve the avocado and add 1 teaspoon
of honey and 2 drops of lemon juice.

*If you are unable to find an avocado, substitute a banana
instead.*

If you are planning to do a lot of home treatments, invest in a
face sauna. They are not particularly expensive and do a
thorough job of drawing out impurities and toning the skin.
However, as I mentioned earlier, I am a great believer in having
a professional treatment once in a while if you can afford it. Not
only will it benefit your skin, but it will give you the opportunity
to relax, unwind and be thoroughly pampered. Most cities have a
number of salons where you should be able to get a one-hour
session for a moderate amount of money and, frankly, if you
smoke or spend money on sweets or snacks you could consider
sacrificing that for the sake of a 'treat' for your face – I'm quite
sure it would be worth it!

ALTHOUGH it is the face that requires the most care and attention, that does not mean you should ignore the rest of your body. While many of us take the trouble to avoid using soap – or at least use only gentle brands – on our faces, we rub our bodies perhaps two or three times a day with the harshest of soaps, which dry out the body skin. I'm sure there are times when your skin feels very dry and flaky, maybe even itchy with dryness. If this is the case, invest in a good glycerine or super-fatted soap for the body, or buy a gentle shower gel. Also remember that it's not necessary to soap the body every time you bath or shower (although obviously, if you are very dirty, soap is necessary). Try using instead a big loofah or even a coarse flannel and rub the body all over with warm water. Use a tough, massaging movement to stimulate the body's circulation while removing dead skin cells. A gentle soap or cleanser is best for the genital areas and under the arms where sweat can build up.

Use a very light oil in your bath water – essential oils are ideal. I have a friend who uses a teaspoon of olive oil. I can't say I like the smell much and it is quite a heavy oil, but she finds it leaves her skin feeling very soft. She also has a job washing out the bath tub!

After your bath or shower, give the body a thorough dosing with a rich cream. There are various body lotions on the market, or a very basic cream from the chemist will do. It is worth making this a regular part of your skin care routine.

Hands

It is surprising how many people exclude hands and feet from their beauty routine. I give my hands a 'session' once a week – or else have them done during my weekly facial.

A home manicure is simple, but to do a thorough job you should have all the 'tools' ready before you begin. So, line up a bowl of warm water, an emery board, orange stick and cuticle-remover, nail polish remover, nail polish and hand cream. If you are in a hurry a nail polish drying-spray may also be useful.

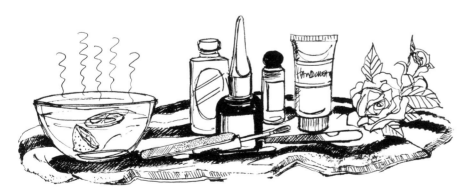

1 File down your nails with the emery board before putting them in water, as warm, soft nails can easily go ragged when filed. I like to wear my nails short; long nails look very old-fashioned to me now. I file them down to a little dome, leaving just a sliver of nail above the finger pad. I think this is a flattering shape for most hands. Certainly, plump hands look neater and prettier with short, well-shaped nails.

2 Soak a pad of cotton-wool in nail polish remover and with this thoroughly rub off all the old polish, pushing the cotton-wool down from the root of the nail. Be careful to remove all the old polish – the residue of several coats of polish piled up on a nail looks so unsightly.

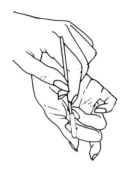

3 Rub cuticle-remover on the cuticles and use an orange stick with cotton-wool over the end to push back the cuticles gently. Don't force them.

4 Soak your hands for a few minutes in a bowl of warm water. This will remove the chemicals you have used on your nails and also soften and cleanse your hands. Wash hands with a gentle soap.

5 Moisturize the hands with two coats of rich cream. Rub in the first coat very thoroughly, then repeat, wiping off any residue.

6 Remove any moisturizing cream which remains on the nails, and apply polish. I tend to use a clear varnish for every day and a colour for special occasions. Apply a thin coat first and allow it to dry *absolutely* before adding a second coat. If you are in a desperate hurry, use a drying spray, although, frankly, this seems to me an unnecessary expense since flapping the hands in the air dries them within a couple of minutes.

Legs

I am fair and do not need to worry much about leg hair, but I know plenty of people do. The cheapest way of removing leg hair is by shaving. Many people used to disapprove of this method because it was said to make the hair grow back thicker. That idea has been discredited now, but there is still a disadvantage to shaving in that initially the hairs grow back as blunt stubble. However, if you shave your legs every two or three days this shouldn't be a problem. A simple – although a little messy – way to remove unwanted hair is to use depilatory creams. The cream is smeared over the leg and then left for about ten minutes, during which time it weakens the hair which will then come away when the leg is scraped clean with a wooden spatula.

You could always have your legs waxed, a quick and painless method these days, but you would be advised to have it done professionally.

Feet

Feet also need careful attention if they are to look good. Like my hands, my feet receive a pedicure once a week. The process is quite similar to the manicure.

1 Soak the feet in warm water and then with a small nailbrush rub hard around the toes to remove any grime (you could also do this to your hands, but I'm assuming your hands will not be as dirty as feet tend to get!)

2 With the brush or a piece of pumice stone, rub any hard areas of skin so as to soften them.

3 Dry the feet and clip the nails. Because toenails are much tougher than fingernails, it is better to clip them when they are soft.

4 Rub feet with cream to soften them; be generous with it on the hard areas. You may like, too, to sprinkle some talcum powder between the toes to make sure the skin there is quite dry.

5 Apply two coats of nail polish to the toes. I like vivid-coloured polish on the toes. I think bright toenails peeking out of open-toe shoes or sandals look glamorous and sexy!

A weekly treatment such as I have outlined should keep your feet looking good. But it is also important to care for their general condition, something I have become very conscious of since I took up dancing. If my feet become damaged or sore I just cannot dance and that, of course, is disastrous when I am appearing in a show. So I choose my shoes very carefully. Even if you are not going to dance, you should make sure your shoes are supportive and a comfortable fit.

Like many of my friends, I used to push my feet into high, pointed shoes and then wonder why my feet and back ached. Such shoes are extremely bad for you because they throw the back out of line and crunch up the toes, so distorting the feet and making you walk badly. I now wear flat shoes when I can. They are wonderfully comfortable and, of course, are very fashionable. Sometimes I wear espadrilles or pumps with a low heel because I like a bit of height, especially with a skirt. I do still dress up in high-heeled shoes for special events, but I try to wear them for shorter periods – and when I'm going to be sitting down for most of the time. Around the house I often go barefoot which is beneficial to the feet because they can relax, and it gives me a chance to flex the toes and generally release any tension. If your floors are too cold for that, try the open Japanese sandals which allow the feet lots of space for stretching.

CARING FOR YOUR SKIN IN THE SUN

LIKE many people I love the sun and can't resist sunbathing. Although I know my skin would be a lot happier if it was never exposed to the sun, I am not prepared to sacrifice the pleasure sunbathing gives me! During breaks from work I spend as much time as possible heading for the beaches or for the countryside where I can enjoy being outdoors. My daughter loves it too. Carly and I have spent many happy summers together building sandcastles and paddling. But at the same time I always take great care to safeguard our skin as best I can.

A sun-tan looks attractive. My skin goes a honey-coloured shade and I gets lots of freckles on my nose. I remember how in my teens I hated freckles; I wanted to look sophisticated and they seemed too girlish and fresh-complexioned. But now I actually like them – and at my age can hardly complain at the idea of looking girlish! Besides, freckles these days are very fashionable, quite in keeping with the vogue for looking fit and healthy.

It's difficult somehow to believe that the sun is harmful. Its warmth seems so comforting and friendly, but let it get underneath your beguiling exterior, believe me, and it will be an absolute fiend, though not many of us are prepared to avoid it since a tan does look so attractive! I've read many times of how Coco Chanel knocked Society sideways when she first started appearing with a tan during the Thirties, a time when women would go to great lengths to remain lily-white.

What the Sun's Rays Do

Many people believe, as I did for years, that we tan because the sun's rays burn the surface of the skin. But, in fact, that is not what happens at all. When the sun's rays penetrate the deepest layers of the skin, they cause melanin – the pigment – to be stimulated and to rise to the surface. When this happens we appear darker, because the pigment has become stronger; luckily, Nature has arranged things so that this darkening also provides some protection for the skin.

However, besides giving you a glowing tan, too much sun can damage the delicate connective tissues. It can also cause wrinkles, dryness and broken capillaries, all of which are irreversible effects, so clearly it makes sense to be careful.

When your skin is exposed to the sun, the blood vessels dilate. And when the skin has an overdose of sun, the tiny blood vessels in the dermis dilate too much and a few hours later they allow blood serum to get into the skin tissues and swell the dermis. This accounts for the tight, sore sensation of sunburn.

It is generally agreed that when you first expose to the sun a body which has kept dressed and hidden for several months, it should be for no more than five or ten minutes at a time. I know it is tempting to think that a few more minutes won't harm you, and of course the first time you go out in the sun you probably won't feel its effect, but the fact is that it *will* harm. During the first week, add another five minutes each day and if you are in a Mediterranean kind of climate with temperatures in the 70s to 80s Fahrenheit make sure your sunbathing is before 10 a.m. or after 4 p.m. Afterwards, put on a blouse and some loose harem trousers, or a long skirt and a hat. I know it isn't fun dressing up when you are getting your first taste of real heat in a long while – but the results if you don't are even less fun!

Once you have a reasonable coating of a tan – a bit like a toffee apple I always think – you can stay in the sun longer. You will reach your optimum tan after about two weeks, and are then unlikely to tan any more. The colour you go depends on the amount of melanin your skin produces – not on the hours spent baking!

It is essential to use a protective sun lotion. There are many good sun products on the market now, designed for every type of skin from the hardy, dark-coloured skin – olive, for example, which tans fairly painlessly – to the very fair, delicate skin such as redheads often have. It is worthwhile buying one formulated for your skin type and you should use it conscientiously. I know far too many people who splash out on all sorts of wonderful-sounding potions and lotions, use them for the first couple of days, and then stop bothering.

Many preparations are numbered, with high numbers generally intended for very pale skin and the lower numbers for darker skin that requires less protection. You will probably find a lower number suitable by the end of a holiday even if you started with something higher. But it's always better to aim for too much protection rather than too little.

And do remember that although the face is the most delicate part of the skin and therefore needs special care, the rest of your body requires attention too. Cover your whole body very thoroughly with oil or cream when you begin sunbathing, top up after *every* swim and then re-apply at regular intervals. You may also find, as I do, that it's worth investing in some additional products, such as a protective cream for the eyelids, or a block for protecting the nose. So many people get badly burnt noses, and although it may not look very glamorous to have a chalky-white painted nose, I think it's probably worth it. Lip cover is something else I consider worthwhile. Burnt, dried lips are very, very uncomfortable and look unattractive. It is possible to buy a tube of gel which protects the lips and also acts as a clear lip gloss. Lipstick works fairly well too, but is inclined to melt in hot sun, so it doesn't offer such thorough protection.

Another important point to remember is that you are exposed to the sun's powerful rays even when you are in the shade or under water, so it is essential to be diligent when using the protective potions.

I'm a great believer in after-sun creams. I always shower after spending time on the beach – which leaves me feeling refreshed and cleansed of sand of salt – and then I cream my body very thoroughly with a basic cream from the chemist. Or you can buy creams specially formulated for use after being in the sun. Some of the most soothing contain coconut oil. A good dose applied to the body will keep the skin supple and help prevent dryness which leads to peeling and scaling. Although you will not entirely repay the moisture that has been stripped from the skin, the cream will help.

If you have the time and money, before going on holiday it's worth undergoing a course of sun ray treatments. Many salons now use a lamp which, it is claimed, cuts out the UV-B rays. These are the rays which are believed to burn and harm the skin. The latest lamps let through only the UV-A rays which colour the skin by bringing the melanin to the skin's surface, and this, of course, means you will have some protection when you first go into the sun.

A shady hat is a must for strong sunshine.

MAKE-UP

I LOVE using make-up. When I have a box of colours and lots of brushes in front of me I'm a child again – free to experiment and paint whatever 'picture' I like! That's why make-up is so delightful these days: just as clothes have become imaginative and inventive, so too have the different styles of make-up.

We have seen a make-up revolution in the past decade: amazing street styles where make-up is used almost as tribal decoration rather than as a discreet way of improving the face. Punks, new romantics, the Japanese fashions and the pop world have all given us extraordinary ideas on how make-up can be extended to face-painting. The idea of using the face as a canvas has caught on and has even affected the more conventional style of make-up in that the big cosmetic companies are now producing all kinds of vivid colours, strange-toned highlighters and blushers to satisfy the current demand. Although I have never gone in for these bizarre make-up styles myself, I do enjoy seeing them on others.

I don't approve, however, of the way make-up seems to trap some people into actually disliking their unmade-up faces. I know people who won't go out without being made-up for fear they will meet someone they know and be 'revealed' as far less glamorous than they normally appear. Agreed that make-up is a wonderful aid on those days when you feel pale and jaded, but I would hate to think that my face was unacceptable without its paint.

I actually spend most of my time when at home during the day unmade-up, because I like the clean, natural feeling of bare skin. I couldn't care less if anyone calls – if they've seen me made-up the night before and don't like the day-time version, well that's too bad. I do think I have more to offer than a decorated face!

Make-up is a wonderful tool for creating different effects. I well know from my modelling days how a beautifully made-up face can look just stunning before the camera. However much I plead the right of my face to be scrubbed clean at home, I know that the fashion pictures and stage pictures of me would not have had the same effect without make-up. That's something Hollywood has known since the beginning of the century. The American writer, Penny Stallings, has written entertainingly of

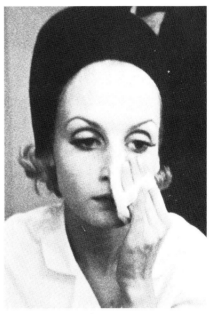

I think these photographs of the tricks you can achieve with make-up speak for themselves. What great fun I had doing these.

how film stars' particular looks were created with make-up. And it was, of course, the Hollwood make-up man who invented lip gloss, false fingernails, hair sprays, setting lotions, body make-up, false eyelashes and hair dyes.

While modelling, I found it fascinating having my face made-up to suit the different fashions and the changing times. Sometimes though I hated what was done to me but it was all part of the job and looking back, it has taught me a great deal about how versatile make-up is.

Remember though that while spending time on an elaborate make-up can be fun once in a while, a good basic make-up should take only minutes. The secret is to have all your cosmetics, brushes and applicators (which should be clean) and any other items such as cotton-wool or concealer stick, laid out ready. I recall once having my make-up done in five minutes flat before going on the Bob Hope Show – and I think I looked fine!

It is not necessary to spend a fortune on cosmetics. A lot of money goes into packaging and advertising the more expensive makes – which in turn pushes up the cost! It's a real 'Catch 22' situation. It's worth knowing that cosmetic manufacturers often produce two or three ranges of varying prices for a company, but with much the same ingredients. It may be that the more expensive product gets a bit of perfume or extra emollient, but quite honestly when it comes to the surface colour there isn't much point in going to the top end of the market. I do, however, buy expensive eye shadows and blushers because then you can often find the best choice of colours. I economize on mascara, lipstick and basic eye-shadow colours for highlighting.

I think Rita Hayworth was my
favourite 'film star' look.

IT is important to be courageous with make-up. It's all too easy to stick with the same style for years, usually a very safe, subtle look which may lift your face a bit but probably won't turn any heads in the street! It's a shame to be so inhibited because changing your make-up can be as stimulating as changing your fashion style.

Over the years I have experimented with all kinds of faces, from the hard look of the Sixties with black lines surrounding the eyes, to the fragile, pale look at the beginning of the Seventies when Gatsby-style clothes were all the rage, to the natural, unmade-up look of today which, is almost more difficult to achieve and often requires more products than lavish stage make-up.

Nowadays during the day I tend to use make-up just to add a tiny bit of emphasis to my face. I might put a line of colour with a soft pencil along the edge of the lashes on the lower lid, apply a smudge of subtle-coloured eye-shadow over the lid and perhaps a thin coat of mascara on my eyelashes; if I'm feeling pale I usually brush a little blusher over my cheeks. When going out in the evening I go for a strong, dramatic look: a mix of coloured shadows, lines around the eyes, highlight shadow on the brow bone and several coats of mascara.

I don't feel I need a single Twiggy 'look' as I did when younger. Now that I feel I know my face and am confident about it, I am able to give it different looks. I think it's important to study your face, learn its features and decided whether you think they need dressing up or down. Assess what kind of effect would work best on your particular assembly of nose, eyes, mouth, cheeks and jaw.

It's all too easy to be seduced by the look of a made-up face in a fashion shot, a magazine or book, and think that's exactly how you want to look. But you must remember that make-up for such photographs is generally done by a skilled make-up artist using numerous products, and will almost certainly be exaggerated because that's what makes effective pictures. By all means, gain inspiration from the fashion pictures around, because they do give guidance as to new looks to aim for, new colours to try, new techniques to experiment with, but don't expect to achieve exactly the same effect – you would in any case probably look rather odd in ordinary daylight!

Looking dramatic. A hint of veil, I think.

The make-up products you buy will depend on the effect you want to achieve. It's worth regarding your make-up collection a bit like your wardrobe. You want a good range of basic products for every day and some more ornate, flamboyant items for evenings and special occasions.

Find a way of experimenting with make-up before you actually buy. You don't want to discover afterwards that frosted grape looks less effective on your eyelids than it did on the counter, and that vibrant red blusher turns you out looking like a clown!

For people who can get to larger cities there are places set up just for this. Joan Price, for example, runs the wonderful Face Place in Central London, a beauty salon where you can have a whole range of treatments and a professional make-up. There are also cosmetics by almost every well known company with which you are free to experiment. They also offer a make-up lesson and Joan will devise for you a personal colour chart. And at Cosmetics à la Carte, also in London (but they are currently negotiating to open in New York), they make up a huge range of their own cosmetics which you can try out at leisure. You can then buy the products you like and if there's a colour you want which is not there, they will make it up for you. You can even go back for refills. Estée Lauder give make-up classes and, in America, the Merle Norman Cosmetic Company hold classes at their many branches throughout the country.

Most large stores have tester cosmetics on display and theoretically you can try before you buy, but the problem here is that usually there are only tiny mirrors to peer into. Also, I find it rather embarrassing splodging eye shadow on lids or rubbing in cream blusher as busy shoppers push past gawping! But be determined. Quite often I try a couple of products, walk off and look for a bigger mirror, have a good look in that, and then decide if I want the item.

Many stores also offer advice, which can be very helpful, but don't allow yourself to be pressurized by sales talk into buying something you don't like. Look at the assistant before you follow her guidance completely; some of them seem to be extraordinarily made-up, with layers of foundation, powder and several coats of eye make-up and lipstick. Frankly, I would hate to look like that, and too much make-up is far more likely to age you than to make you appear younger. Stores sometimes offer to make you up, but it's worth making clear beforehand the kind of look you are after. Don't be too inflexible though – often the assistant will make valuable suggestions.

FOUNDATION, as the name suggests, is the basis of your make-up. It's quite possible to wear blusher, eye make-up and lip colour without foundation, but you won't achieve that very clear, fresh look which it gives to the skin. The aim of foundation is to make your face into a clear, smooth surface, to which you can apply colour to bring out the sparkle in your eyes, the whiteness of your teeth and to emphasize the colour and sheen of your hair. It also protects your complexion from the effects of wind, cold, pollution, dirt and dust. It was once thought that foundation blocked the pores, but this is not true – at least, not if you clean it off properly at night. It can and does clog pores if it's left on while you are asleep and your skin needs to breathe.

Choosing the right foundation is most important. They come in a variety of forms: liquid, cream, mousse, emulsion texture, and a cake-like texture. My favourite is a creamy liquid which contains moisturizer but has enough body actually to coat my face. But when I am going out in the evening or am appearing on stage, I use a heavier cream make-up.

If you have greasy skin, look for an oil-free foundation or one with very little oil – you don't want something which will add to the oiliness of your face and a lot of foundations do contain moisturizer. Often the kind suitable for greasy skin comes in a liquid or cream formula, so check when you buy that you have the right kind. Matt make-ups reduce shine and may well be suitable for your skin. Seek the advice of a beauty consultant in a store or at a salon.

If you have dry or normal skin, choose a foundation containing emollient: the formula should be one based on water in oil, but avoid any which make the skin too slippery, or which vanish completely because they contain too much moisturizer.

The colour of your foundation is all-important. When I started modelling, many people – particularly older women – wore pink and peach foundation to give colour to their faces. That's no longer fashionable, thank goodness. Coloured foundations may look attractive in the bottle but because of your body's temperature and your own natural colouring, foundations often change colour when applied to the face – which is why it's important always to test before buying. Go to a shop where there are testers on display and try some on your jaw or neck to see how well it blends with your skin. (Testing colour on the inside of your wrist or hand just doesn't work – it's not truly representative of how it will look on your face.) A natural-looking foundation is best. Neutral shades – stone, beige or a dull cream – are popular because they do look natural. They reduce redness and provide a good basis for colour. Only people with sallow skin should choose foundation with some colour.

How to Apply Foundation

After cleansing and moisturizing your face, apply small dots of foundation to cheeks, nose, forehead and chin, and work gently into the skin with either your fingertips or a complexion sponge. Do not rub the complexion or pull the skin. Barbara Daly the make-up expert suggests putting foundation on the back of the hand and using this as a palette, then taking up just a little at a time and applying with a sponge. The foundation should not be applied as a thick coat but as a thin coating through which natural colour will emerge. The aim is to achieve a uniform colour and texture all over the face.

POWDER

APPLYING powder is an excellent way of 'setting' your foundation if it has got to last throughout the day or evening in a warm atmosphere. Powder used always to be coloured, so that it provided a pink or peach topping to foundation and all too often made the face look rather lurid. Nowadays, colourless and translucent powders are available, and I much prefer these because they simply give a matt finish to the foundation without adding colour and leave the face looking far more natural.

When choosing your powder compare several varieties carefully. Joan Price pointed out to me that many so-called colourless powders are in fact no such thing. So test several on the back of your hand on top of a little foundation rubbed in, to see which really does appear to provide a colourless coating.

I prefer loose powders because compressed compact powders tend to be coloured and leave a much heavier finish.

How to Apply Powder

I use a large, soft brush to apply my powder. I dust it all over my face then with a clean brush I go over the face once again, removing any excess. You could also use a soft puff – the old-fashioned swansdown variety feels lovely – or a big ball of cotton-wool. Using just a brush, however, creates a less 'made up' and therefore more natural finish. You could dust only the nose and perhaps the forehead if they are extra oily areas, and leave the rest of the complexion unpowdered.

BLUSHER

YOUR blusher will set the colour tone for your face. If you are going for a natural look, then something like a peach, a pale rose-pink or a beige-pink will give just a hint of colour. The earthy terracotta, brown and dark beige shades also give a natural colour. They don't look very inspiring in their boxes, I know, but you may well find that on the cheeks they look better than the cruder bright pinks, red and peaches.

Blushers come in several forms – either as powder, grease, liquid, cream or gel. If your skin is very greasy, it is probably best to use a powder; for dry or normal skin it doesn't matter which you use. I like a cream or liquid colour if I am wearing just foundation and want a slightly shiny, natural look. And sometimes, if I am not wearing foundation at all, I just rub a bit of colour onto the cheekbones – this works well in summer when I have a tan. Powder blusher is best over the top of a powdered complexion and will last well. You can't, successfully, put cream or liquid colour on top of powder.

How to Apply Blusher

Blushers are applied to the cheekbone to create an illusion of hollowness. I make an inverted triangle of colour on the face by drawing a line, about one-and-a-quarter inches, along the cheek, up to a point just above the level of my nostril, then take the line out again and down. I use either a powder brush-on blusher or the cream and liquid variety.

Soft texture blusher can be applied just to the cheekbone and gently rubbed over the area immediately below to give a soft natural glow to the face. If you want a very light colour, try mixing a little liquid blusher and foundation together and apply lightly with the fingertips to the cheek area.

EYE MAKE-UP

APPLYING eye make-up is, to me, the most exciting stage of my make-up routine. With clever make-up, eyes can be made to look large and beautiful, bright and gleaming.

Eye-Shadows

At one time it was thought that you should match eye shadow to your eye colour, but now people use all kinds of different colours, and often get the best results from eye-shadows which contrast with their own colour. For example, Beverley Sassoon suggests trying golden-brown above blue eyes because it actually makes the eyes look bluer. And I find purple and slate-grey go well with my eyes which are a grey-blue. I also wear blue at times.

If you wear several eye colours together, choose a basic lid colour that tones in with your clothes. For example, you might use brown to line the lid and a pinky-brown pearlized shadow over the brow bone, then a purple shadow on the lid to go with clothes in lilac, mauve or purple. Or with the same basic eye colours, you could use a yellow-gold shadow on the lids to tone with yellow or greeny-yellow clothes. And so on.

This method, however, doesn't work so well with very bright primary colours. For example, if I wear a scarlet or electric-blue sweater I tend to use muted neutral shades on my eyes, otherwise the effect is too much.

For me, eye make-up has always been exciting.

Sometimes I mix together two or even three shadows in different colours on my lids. For example, I might use a light lilac in a v-shape, going from the inside point of the eye out to cover one-third of the lid, then I apply a smoky-grape shade to cover the central portion of the lid and finally, I take a smoky blue with some purple in it for the outer edge of the eye. I use a medium-tipped brush for the central and outer areas, and a fine one for the inside point of the eye. The colours are 'painted' on in bars and then, with my finger, I smooth them together. I find this gives a softer look than just the one colour.

I think it's wonderful that there are no definite rules nowadays on which eye colours can and cannot be worn. Colours which were once only used on cheeks – such as the fuchsia blusher given me by Barbara Hulanicki – are now used on eyes to create stunning effects. I love the theatrical products, such as Stagelight make, where many colours are shot through with silver or gold dust to give an amazing sheen. These are really most suitable for evenings but occasionally, if I'm feeling high-spirited, I take a tiny, fine-tipped brush and run a line of, say, shocking pink mixed with cobalt along the eyelid.

Eye-shadows come in different textures: powder, cream, gloss, liquid, or in block form requiring water, like in a paintbox. The creamy ones go on beautifully and blend in to give a very soft colour, but if you are going anywhere warm they tend to melt into the creases of the skin and form 'pockets' of colour. I particularly like the loose powder variety because you can achieve a very thin coating of colour with these. The block powder or liquid colours need careful application but they look great if you are aiming for a defined effect.

Eye-pencils

Eye-pencils are one of the great inventions, in my opinion. I use them to line the upper and lower lids of my eyes and also to draw lines above the crease of the eye. I particularly like the very soft kohl pencils which originate from India where they are used to create a smudged effect around the eye. This gives a lovely sensual look, except when used to draw heavy dark rims around the eyes – I think that looks dreadful. My favourite eye-pencil colour is a vivid emerald-green.

Mary Quant do an excellent range of pencils in what they call 'cocktail' colours, all very bright and dazzly. I particularly like the one with vivid electric-blue one end and a bright, shocking pink the other – for evenings you can use both colours around the eyes and make a real impression!

Eye-liners   Eye-liners come in either block form or as liquid or cream. They are useful for painting an extremely fine dark line along the upper rim of the eye where the eyelashes grow. This gives the eyes a very clear shape and lots of emphasis.

Mascara   Just as a hat completes a striking outfit, so mascara is the finishing touch to your eye make-up. The easiest kinds to use, I find, are the roll-on liquid variety, but I am wary of those which contain tiny filaments because these can drop off and irritate the eyes. Mascara also comes in easy-to-apply tubes with little brushes. Another type, the block and brush, so popular when my mum was bringing me up, you rarely, if ever, see nowadays.

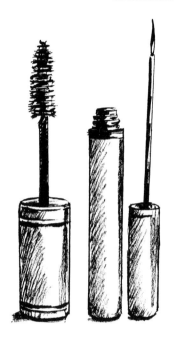

If you are planning to be out in all weathers, or to go swimming, it is sensible to buy a waterproof mascara. But you will need an oily remover to get it off, and there is a risk here of the oil around the eyes causing puffiness. If this happens, change your mascara and do without it when you go in the water.

Check the mascara you use does not smudge. Little looks worse than dark rings around the eyes where mascara has rubbed off. An alternative, of course, to using mascara, is to have your eyelashes dyed (I don't recommend doing it yourself), although this won't give the added thickness you get with mascara.

How to Apply Eye Make-Up

I have a positive army of brushes and soft-topped applicators in many different shapes and sizes. I find them all essential, and they enable me to use one colour in, say, a broad band, while with a fine-tipped brush I can apply just a fine streak of another colour. For best results, follow these simple stages:

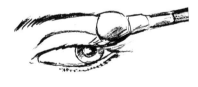

1 Begin by applying a water-based, pale ivory eye gloss over the whole eye area, as a foundation for other colours. This will help to counteract melting and creasing which occurs with the cream and grease eye colours. Smooth on gently with the tip of the finger or a sponge-tipped applicator.

2 Apply highlighter colour, in perhaps a frosted or pearlized light shade, above the crease of the eye going out towards the brow bone. If you use powder shadow, smooth in gently with a blunt-ended brush, otherwise use a sponge-tipped applicator or your finger.

One of Barbara Daly's famous make-up sessions.

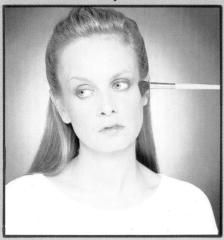 

The correct placing of blusher accentuates cheekbones, and will enhance the structure of your face.

Barbara always outlines lips before filling in the colour – this stops it from 'bleeding'.

3 For extra emphasis, with an eye-pencil run a line of colour along the crease of the eye and rub in with your finger to soften and blend with the higher colour.

4 Apply dominant colour to the eyelid by stroking over the entire lid with brush, applicator or finger. Two or even three shadows in different shades mixed together can look very effective.

5 If you are using an eye pencil or liner, apply it in a thin line along the upper lid of the eye. You could also apply it to the lid before the eye shadow so that the shadow blends with it. Make sure your pencil is sharpened to a fine point, or use a fine-tipped brush.

6 To give eyes a very bright, slightly startled look, run a line of vividly coloured pencil along the inside rim of the bottom lid where the eyelashes begin, particularly effective if you use the metallic and shiny pencils.

7 Apply mascara in thin coats. Using applicator or brush, stroke the colour on to the lashes from the eye lid outwards. Let one coat dry before applying another. Avoid putting on thick coats because these will probably clog, to cause thick, heavy, spiky lashes – not very attractive!

LIP COLOUR

I DON'T wear lipstick all the time but I love the effect of a really vivid, glossy mouth if I'm going out somewhere special – otherwise, I might wear a coat of colourless or slightly pink lip gloss during the day. And if I am going out in either very cold or hot weather, to prevent my lips drying I use Elizabeth Arden's 8-Hour Cream, which is colourless and quite thick and provides a sheen for the lips which does not easily get removed.

Lipstick comes in grease form in the traditional roll-up cases; in narrow sticks, pencils and in grease block form which you apply with a brush. There are also lip glosses, usually in small containers, which you apply with brush or finger. Most cosmetic houses have several ranges covering the fairly classic red, pink, orange and peach shades, and also the more unusual plum, grape, cinnamon, vivid pink and frosted and translucent colours requested by younger people.

(Opposite) **The finished result. OK?**

For a well-defined mouth which will keep its colour, first outline the mouth with a lipstick pencil or a fine brush which you dip into the product. Then fill in the outline with your lipstick or again use brush or a lipstick pencil. Try a colour a couple of tones lighter than the outlining colour. Many professionals find that lipstick applied with a brush is the most effective way of making colour stay fast. Finally, apply a fine coat of transparent lip gloss with a brush. Or use one of the lip-fixing products now available.

Lip gloss on its own does not require an outline and can be applied with the finger for a soft, smudgy effect. If you want it to look more precise, use a brush.

EYEBROWS

I F applying mascara is like putting on a hat, then keeping the eyebrows in order is like having a good hair-cut – it really is important if you want your total make-up to look good. Straggly, mis-shapen brows can be remarkably powerful in their impact!

There was a trend for women to pluck their brows into narrow, high-arched curves, or to pluck out all the natural hair and them draw in sweeping, femme fatale brows. Both looked quite dreadful in my view. What you are aiming for are natural-looking brows, to provide a frame for your eyes.

Some people have ill-shaped, unruly eyebrows, in which case it may be necessary to remove quite a lot of hair, but even so you can still try to create a shape which is in line with the way the hair grows. The best shape for most faces is a low, neat arc, slightly thicker (but only slightly) at the inner corner of the eye, which becomes a little thinner in texture as it reaches the outer edge of the eye. The arc comes over the whole body of the eye.

Pluck your eyebrows with tweezers, pressing firmly on the flesh just above where you want to remove the hair – this will help to numb the sensation. Then pull quickly. It hurts a little, but really not enough to worry you. When you have tidied your eyebrows you may feel they need some emphasis. In this case, use a light pencil – I go for a light grey but never a colour which would make my eyebrows seem drawn in – and brush it over the hairs. Alternatively, you could use a powder colour to brush over the arc.

I KEEP a large selection of cosmetics at home – I don't believe in throwing away products just because they are from last season. Consequently, I have an assortment which fills a small suitcase, but I use them all, sometimes mixing several together to create my own unusual shades.

Obviously, I don't want to take them all with me every time I'm out for the evening, so I have a small make-up bag which fits into my handbag and contains my 'emergency kit'. Into this go: a tube of foundation; a small brush-on blusher compact with mirror; powder compact in as neutral a shade as possible; three eyeshadows in neutral shades; eye-pencil in a dark, smoky blue; wand mascara; transparent lip gloss; small packet of face cleansing pads and a tiny tube of moisturizer.

With my 'emergency kit', which really doesn't take up much space, I know I can repair my make-up whenever necessary.

ALLERGIES

MOST of us are able to use almost any make-up without problems – chiefly because cosmetic manufacturers test their products extensively before putting them on the market – but inevitably a few people do react badly. If you find your eyes becoming red and sore when you make them up, your skin feeling sore, tight or coming out in spots or unexpected marks after you have applied foundations, it is probably worth trying one of the hypo-allergenic ranges. Many of the leading cosmetic houses now do these ranges, and they really are no more expensive than ordinary products.

CAMOUFLAGE

I F you have small marks, blemishes, little scars or shadows which you want to minimize, it is worth learning the tricks for doing so. Barbara Daly explains that to cover dark shadows, marks and lines you need something lighter; blemishes that are paler than your skin tone should be shaded down to match it. She suggests a special camouflage stick or a cream foundation which is a shade lighter than your skin tone.

First, apply your basic foundation. Then very gently with the camouflage stick, or a fine-tipped brush if you are using foundation, paint the colour on to the area – immediately under the eyes, for instance, where many of us have shadows, or down the sides of the nose; the inner eye corners also often look dark and can be improved with a tiny touch of light foundation. Next, blend the colour in, but be very gentle if you are working around the eyes.

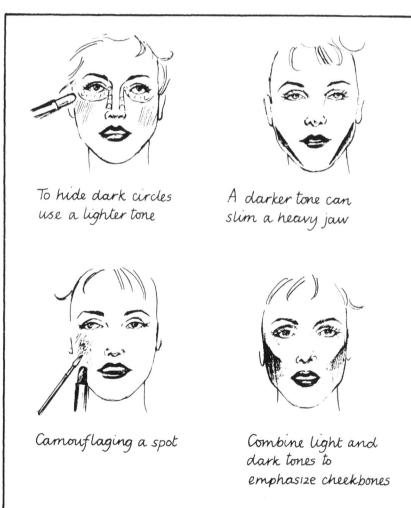

To hide dark circles use a lighter tone

A darker tone can slim a heavy jaw

Camouflaging a spot

Combine light and dark tones to emphasize cheekbones

Make-up to achieve a special effect. Here as Cockney flower girl, Eliza of Pygmalion.

HAIR

EVER since I was a small girl and my mum cut off my long hair because a neighbour said it would give me dizzy spells, I've had a passion for growing my hair really long – right down my back. I don't know why. Why *does* one develop these passions? Perhaps long hair fulfils a childhood fantasy about how girls are supposed to look. Anyway, now that I've finally done it I'm satisfied, but I'm beginning to wonder whether I should have it cut into a new style!

I started growing my hair in 1971, and it took about seven years before it was really long. Growing hair seems to take ages, so it's not surprising that many people become disheartened and give up.

There are many old wives' tales of how to make hair grow more quickly – from brushing it 100 times a day to rubbing in different potions. But the simple fact is that none of this helps. There are about 120,000 hairs on an average head, and each grows approximately half an inch a month. Some hair may grow a little bit faster than this and some may grow more slowly, but that is decided by Nature. If you want to grow your hair, the only practical thing you can do is to follow a sensible diet. As with the rest of our bodies, our hair – both the condition and growth rate – is affected by the food we eat.

The most difficult thing is sticking to your decision. I remember when I was first growing my hair I was quite determined for a long time, but then gave in, although it wasn't exactly my fault. I had been signed up by Ken Russell to do the film of *The Boy Friend*. At the time I had just started to grow my hair and had a vivid picture in my mind of the beautiful long mane I would have one day. But then Ken asked me to cut my hair. I said no. He said yes. We had a big fight and of course he won – he was tougher than me, as well as being the director! Well, in the end I had to admit that he was right. It was a 1920s movie and the short style was just perfect.

It is difficult for many of us to stick to our resolve to grow our hair because it usually looks so ghastly at the in-between stage. It's easiest if you have short, all-one-length cut so that your hair grows down like a curtain, then you just need to have the ends trimmed regularly to keep it in shape. But a layered cut is much harder. Layers which grow out do not usually lie flat and smooth,

This short style was perfect for the 1920s effect of The Boyfriend.

and unless your hair is very curly with lots of body, they won't form a pretty halo. In this case it is best first to have a good cut which will at least make the hair one shape, then once it has grown a bit, try to find a style which works. For example, longish, layered hair looks pretty with uneven, natural-looking curls. With heated rollers this is quite easy to do, although do remember that heated rollers should not be used every day as they will dry the hair.

Another way is to buy a couple of those big bulldog clips which 'clasp' a large chunk of hair. Position the clips, one each side of the head, about one inch from the level of the ears, so as to hold the hair off your face. Or gather up all the hair together, anchor it on top of the head in a little bunch or knot, with wispy bits coming down. This can look very pretty – and often quite sexy!

Have your hair trimmed regularly, at least every couple of months. I fought against doing this when I first started growing my hair because it seemed counter-productive. But I know at least two very good hairdressers – Michael Gottfried in New York and Daniel Galvin in London – who are both most insistent that this is the best way to keep hair looking good. Otherwise split ends will form, and these could split right along the hair shaft, causing damage to all your hair.

It is surprising how hair, which seems short, straggly and, frankly, a complete mess one day, can suddenly appear a decent length just a month or so later. So do persevere – it really doesn't take so long after the first few months to achieve a glamorous head of hair.

ALTHOUGH I like my hair long, I'm not suggesting that everyone should grow theirs. In fact, not everyone can. I know people who have 'let their hair go' for months just to see how long it would get, and their locks have never grown beyond their shoulders. Women with very tight, curly hair often find it won't grow long; and quite often it grows out rather than down, which I think can look tremendous. One girl I know has a pale, heart-shaped face and a huge halo of bright-red, wiry curls which she has grown to chin length. She looks fantastic.

It is vital when choosing a hairstyle to consider your face and physique generally. If you have a long thin face, then probably long straight hair is not right for you. You might do better to have a chin-length bob which swings out into a nice full shape, or a layered cut which makes your hair bouncy and wavy, giving your face breadth.

And a well-defined face with good bone structure can look terrific with a very short, stark hairstyle. How beautiful, for instance, Mia Farrow always looks with her elfin hair-cut. If you have a round face, long, straight hair cut to shoulder-length will suit you, as will a style which leaves hair very short at the sides with height and bounce on top. With a pair of big, bold earrings, this hairstyle can also play down a rather fleshy jaw or puffy cheeks.

You must also consider your hairstyle in relation to the rest of you and to the way you dress. Long, straight hair, parted in the middle and left like a shiny waterfall, for example, looks great on a tall girl or a small, slim girl. But I've never thought such a style does much for the short, slightly plump person. A woman with broad hips and not a lot of bust will suit a well-shaped, smooth cut which tapers down the neck.

But the key to any style is the cut. Hair which is well shaped and balanced looks wonderful. Choosing your style is an individual decision, and no book can give hard and fast rules. If you have a good hairdresser, ask his or her advice. Consider your best facial features and work out what kind of style is likely to accentuate these. Look at pictures of other people with roughly your kind of looks and study their hairstyles, but if you do spot a magazine picture of a style you like, don't demand it from your hairdresser if he or she advises strongly against it. I recall one hairdresser telling me of a woman who came in clutching a glossy shot of a top model; the model's hair was a mass of soft waves, a style specially created for the photography session but not robust enough for daily life. The hairdresser advised against it, and tried tactfully to point out the differences between her face type and hair and those of the model. But the woman would not be moved. So the hairdresser agreed to do his best. He layered her hair and set it, and when she went out she was quite happy. But two days later she returned, absolutely furious, her hair hanging limply around her face.

Having a hairdresser you like, trust and feel will respect what you want, is all-important. It may seem fun to go to the trendiest person in town but that fun soon diminishes if he or she gives you the latest style regardless of your own looks – and it is surprising how often that happens. If you know someone whose hair always seems to look good, it is probably worth giving her hairdresser a try, or ask around and see who is most highly recommended. Bear in mind that very often it is not the most fashionable or expensive hairdresser who is best for you. Many of the smaller salons employ expert cutters who will take the time to get to know you and your hair and are interested in pleasing you.

I remember when I had my hair cut for *The Boy Friend*, I wasn't at all happy with the result. The person who did it, although a competent cutter, just didn't understand my hair. He couldn't get it to lie properly, and I felt very miserable afterwards. So I went to Leonard, who had been doing my hair ever since I began modelling, and he immediately knew how to put it in order.

Very often, one of the reasons people have their hair short is that they don't want to have to bother devising different ways of

When I was on Broadway in *My One and Only*, **my hair was plaited up and pincurled under a scarf to give the impression of a short style, but it could be brushed out quickly as soon as the performance was over.**

wearing it – they like it in the same style for both during the day and going out in the evenings. But if you do want a short style which is versatile, there are several to choose from. A style which is short at the sides and long on top may be worn smooth and brushed off the face by day, but for an evening out you could curl the top part and put a couple of combs in the sides. Or tie a silk scarf, folded into a tubular shape, around your head with a large floppy bow on top. Or blow-dry it very smooth and straight and perhaps 'persuade' a Clara Bow kiss curl with setting lotion or gel.

It suited my lifestyle, while performing in *My One and Only*, to have long hair because I could plait it up under the wig I wore on stage and if I had to go to a restaurant or to a 'do' after the show, I could brush out the plaits and have a bit of wave in my hair.

A style I particularly like for casual occasions, and one which I think suits many people, is a big braid worn down the back. I plait my hair from the nape of my neck quite loosely so that it looks thick. It's very quick to do and stays looking neat all day without needing any attention. Sometimes I make two braids and fix them around my head. I look a bit like Heidi then which isn't quite the image I'm after! It amuses me to be wearing hairstyles which traditionally have been worn by children, while my young daughter sports a very trendy short cut!

I wear my hair up in a knot quite often. That's another effortless style. I usually also pull out a few strands, curl them with a drop of water and then pin them in place to dry. The result is corkscrew curls at the side of my face. Or I just let strands of hair fall naturally. If I want to dress up the knot, I put a scarf around it or add fancy combs.

Sometimes I wear a pony tail, another style which suits most people, and I like the look of it either curled or plaited. For more dressy occasions there are several styles I adopt. A favourite is wearing my hair loose with strands of hair from the sides pulled off my face and held in place at the back with combs or clips. This gives a slightly Renaissance touch. Other times, if I am going somewhere very special, I go for the full Renaissance look, and wear my hair very wild and curly. This does require time and effort, and will work on most hair, although fine, soft hair 'takes' best. For the full effect I make numerous little plaits all over my hair and then sleep in them. When I take the plaits out and comb my hair through it is very bushy and elaborate. To give added strength to the curl, run a little setting lotion or gel and a drop of water through the hair before plaiting.

If I want more controlled curls then I have to sleep in curlers. Luckily, it's not like when I was young, when I can remember feeling tortured all night by horrible, spiky, plastic curlers stuck all over the head. Now I have wonderful, foam-rubber, fabric-covered tubes from Molton Brown in London. These soft, rubber, bendy tubes can also be found in many department stores – you wrap the hair around them and they make it curly.

If you are growing out your fringe, another pretty style I can recommend is to curl the fringe bits and then put up the rest of the hair in a knot or chignon. I quite often pin-curl the front under my wig during a show, then I can go out to dinner afterwards looking quite presentable.

Loose, windswept curls can soften a more formal hairstyle.

THERE are so many things you can do to hair these days, and so many advertisements and articles tempting us to experiment. But before going for a complete change of style, it is sensible to understand what your hair consists of, how it works and what happens to it when you do give it a new treatment. After all, each hair is with us for several years, so it's worth taking the trouble to treat it properly.

Hair is made up of a protein called keratin and it also contains a small, but very vital, amount of water. When that dries up your hair becomes dry, brittle, lifeless – most of us have experienced this and know how impossible it can be to do anything with hair in that state. The strands of hair are remarkably tough – someone once compared them with equal-size strands of copper wire and found that the hair was stronger. Which is just as well when you consider some of the brutal things we do to our hair. I like to think of these strands as a stick of seaside rock. There is an outside coating called the cuticle, which is the hair's tough, protective coating; it acts a bit like a tortoise's shell because it is hard and protects the soft 'body' underneath. The soft centre to the hair shaft, which is a tube within the cuticle, is called the cortex. This contains the hair's melanin – its pigment – and it is this which determines your hair colour.

Our hair type is fixed by our genes, so it's thanks to my mum and dad that I have fair, straight hair. No matter how many times we are told that eating bread crusts will make our hair curly, or any of the other old wives' tales, the fact is that nothing can alter the way our hair has been fixed at conception. If you have straight hair and want curls, they you have got to organize it with chemicals, not Nature.

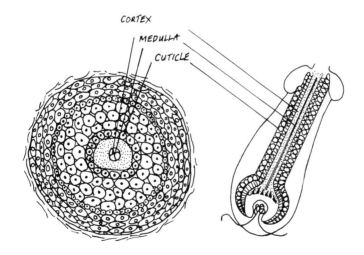

CORTEX
MEDULLA
CUTICLE

CARING FOR YOUR HAIR

A LOT of time and money have been spent on formulating products to suit different hair types, but you cannot benefit from these products until you recognize what your hair type is.

Greasy hair   Generally fine and lank, it is shinier than dry hair because more sebum, the oil present in our hair, forms on the scalp. If it is very greasy, you should wash it every day or even twice a day and condition it only about once a month with an oil-free conditioner. Too much conditioner can make it even greasier. Choose a shampoo containing lemon.

Dry hair   This tends to be dry to the touch, brittle, fly-away and with a tendency to split ends. But when it is washed and conditioned properly it can look very sleek and have the pretty, soft effect of a baby's hair. Wash it whenever necessary with a shampoo containing moisturizer and always use conditioner. A special treatment for dry hair is a good idea about once a month.

Normal hair   This is usually soft, easily manageable and has a natural sheen. It doesn't need much special attention and should be washed whenever seems necessary. Use conditioner every few washes and the occasional special treatment may give it a boost.

Shampoos

A good shampoo is vital for hair to look in condition, have a smashing sheen and be easy to control. A shampoo which doesn't suit your hair can do exactly the opposite. But with so many shampoos on the market it's very hard to know which to choose. And even when you have found the right one don't think you can stick with it all the time because, like skin, hair tires of one product and stops responding to it, so you may suddenly find that hair which for months looked great while you used a particular product, doesn't look as good. This can of course result too from ill health or from being a bit rundown: hair is extremely sensitive to our general well-being and, like a barometer, records our state of health.

I keep a range of shampoos which I know suit my hair and I alternate them. I choose a very gentle shampoo with built-in conditioner – I also use a separate conditioner after – and I particularly like the ones which have herbs or extract of henna in them.

Shampoos were first introduced in the 1930s and in those days they tended to be fairly harsh. A lot of work has gone into improving and refining them which means that it is now possible for them actually to improve damaged hair fibres if they contain conditioning ingredients and do not have too high a percentage of harsh detergents. I was rather shocked to learn that detergent is the basis of most shampoos. Like many people I associate that word with washing powders and the liquid I use for washing dishes – and I can't say I fancy *that* on my locks. Mind you, I did once use washing-up liquid when I was much younger and desperate to wash my hair in time for a date, and there just wasn't any shampoo in the house. The result was horrific. My hair ended up like old rope!

But that is not likely to happen to you. As the American *Consumer's Guide to Cosmetics* explains, the bulk of today's shampoos are made from synthetic detergent which removes grease and dirt from hair just as efficiently as old-fashioned detergents did, but they don't strip it as violently. And even though, like most people, I have had it drummed into me that rinsing off shampoo is most important, many of these products are actually designed to leave a film on the hair to make it manageable.

I remember years ago being told that it was wrong to shampoo your hair more than once a day and although when modelling I often had to do just that, I would try hard at other times to 'last' for several days without a hair wash. The result was my hair became stringy, developed a film of grease and generally looked unattractive. Nowadays it is considered fine to wash your hair as often as you wish and for many people that means daily. I have a friend who swims almost every day and she automatically gives her hair a wash under the shower afterwards. Nothing dreadful seems to have happened as a result!

There are different shampoos to suit the different hair types and it is well worth using these. For instance, shampoos for dry hair frequently contain an oil extract or an ingredient which will add oil to the hair, which I find essential for my dry hair. I know if I use a 'normal' shampoo and no conditioner, my hair becomes very dry and rather fly-away. Another friend with greasy hair looks hard for shampoos which contain lemon or a herb recommended to counteract grease, and she finds that helps to make her hair manageable.

The ingredients in shampoos are advertised as though they can work miracles – they can't. But a shampoo with a mild detergent and a conditioning ingredient is probably necessary for most people – and it really isn't very important whether it is avocado, jojoba or henna. Protein, though, is said to be of great help if your hair is damaged.

You have probably come across shampoos which claim to be pH balanced and have wondered what on earth the pH is and why it needs balancing. In simple terms, 'pH' measures degrees of acidity and alkalinity: the hair has an *acid* mantle which protects it, but this can be damaged by *alkaline* substances – detergent is one – and when this happens the hair becomes dry and dull-looking, which is a signal that the pH balance needs adjusting. Those 'pH-balanced' shampoos are said to be made up in such a way that they maintain the acid mantle on the hair. But I don't find these work any better on my hair than other shampoos specially formulated for dry hair.

People often ask how useful dandruff shampoos are. The answer is really a matter of how serious your dandruff is. If you have a small amount, it can probably be helped by using one of these shampoos which are made with anti-bacterial ingredients, but if the condition persists and is serious, you would be sensible to consult a doctor or even a trichologist.

You still find dry shampoos, although these are not used nearly as much now. They are quite useful if you have long hair and washing it is impossible. But they should only ever be used in an 'emergency' and never as a substitute for washing.

Conditioners   Choosing a conditioner is no easier than choosing a shampoo. Sometimes I have stood and stared in amazement at supermarket rows packed full of conditioners, some of the advertisements for which make the most amazing claims. Consequently, I have become sceptical about advertisements for beauty products because they go far beyond the realm of what is possible.

The function of a conditioner is to coat the hair shafts so as to protect them and to keep in the moisture. Some conditioners actually make the hair shafts appear thicker, which is useful if you have fine hair and not much of it. Some also replace a bit of the sebum, the natural hair usually coating the hair, if it has been removed by, for example, a perm. But there is a limit to what conditioners can do. If you seriously damage and split the hair shaft, then no conditioner can sweep in like a fairy godmother and undo the damage.

The kind of conditioner you choose will obviously depend on

what you want of it. There are conditioners you put on, leave for a minute or two, then rinse off, which are great just for keeping hair in condition, for making it shiny and tangle-free. Then there are conditioners, such as the thick, creamy kinds for dry hair, which replace oil. Protein conditioners have also become very popular for dry hair. These cover the hair shaft, filling in any gaps and holes and leaving it sleek and smooth. It is possible to buy protein packs which you leave on for about twenty minutes. I know that when my hair has been curled and styled a lot, a really intense treatment like this is beneficial.

When I'm working, I like my hair to be simple to deal with.

Sometimes, if I have been messing around with my hair too much or it I have been out in the sun – as bad for hair as it is for skin – I have a proper conditioning treatment. This might be henna wax or perhaps heated oil which is left on the hair for about half an hour. Some hairdressers provide these treatments and I find they give my hair a real boost. It is also possible to buy warm oil treatments and henna wax and apply them yourself at home. These products though can be quite expensive. An ordinary cooking oil will work just as well. Olive oil is one that has been suggested to me, but I find it forms a very thick layer on the hair and is extremely hard to get off. I prefer to use a more easily-absorbed polyunsaturated oil such as corn oil. Rub this through so that your hair is completely covered and has a slightly wet look. Then wrap your hair in a warm towel and leave for at least half an hour. You will probably find it takes two or even three shampoos to remove the oil, and sometimes it is more effective to leave a couple of hours between shampoos. After shampooing, I find it worthwhile to use a cream conditioning-rinse, otherwise it may be difficult to comb through the hair. And after all, the more conditioning your hair has the better, particularly if it has been in a bad state.

Another idea if your hair seems out of condition and very dry, is to rub a little hair cream such as Vitapointe across the surface, but avoiding the scalp.

If you have greasy hair, it will need rather different treatment. Tony and Guy, a salon in London, have looked at the problems of greasy hair and have come up with some suggestions. They recommend that you wash your hair regularly – every day if you can – with a mild shampoo and then rinse off with cold water which will help to close the pores and prevent the oil from coming through. As a final rinse, instead of conditioner, apply a mix of an ounce of cider vineger with seven ounces of water, shaken well in a bottle first. If you dislike the smell of the vinegar, add a few drops of oil of cloves. As an alternative to this, mix eight ounces of citric acid tablets (bought from the chemist or drugstore) with one gallon of water; you then make partings in your hair with a large comb and dab the mixture along the scalp. This should not be rinsed off. Another tip for greasy heads, is to add a tablespoon of lemon juice to a jug of water for the final rinse. This will give your hair a lovely sheen.

Most good hairdressers also have salon treatments for greasy scalps and it is worth investing in one of these regularly if your hair is a problem.

How to Apply Shampoo and Conditioner

Shampoo should be applied in a small dollop – just enough to coat thinly the inner circle of the palm. Too much means a lot of lather and a waste of shampoo. If you have dry or normal hair, massage the shampoo in with the fingertips using a fairly strong touch. If you have greasy hair, rub the shampoo across the scalp gently, as too much vigorous pressure stimulates the sebaceous glands which produce the oil.

After one application rinse the head thoroughly with lukewarm water – hot water can dry hair and harm it. If you are washing your hair every day a single shampoo will probably be adequate, but if your hair is very dirty or greasy, you should repeat the procedure.

After shampooing, apply a conditioner or finishing rinse. Pour it into the palm of your hand – about the same amount as shampoo – and apply to the head, but remember it is the hair not the scalp which needs the conditioner, so do not massage in but rub gently into the hair. If you do rub conditioner into the scalp too often, it may become itchy. If you have very long hair, comb the conditioner through from the bottom upwards. Finally, dry your hair by patting it with a warm, dry towel. Don't rub it violently in the way I remember doing as a child. This just tangles the shafts and means you will have an awful job dragging a comb through. And pulling wet hair is harmful because it stretches and weakens the hair shafts.

Drying and Styling Your Hair

I have used a blow drier on my hair for almost as long as I can remember. It is wonderfully convenient for drying hair quickly and, because the heat of the air straightens out the hair shaft, hair tends to look very smooth and shiny afterwards. But hair driers do have their disadvantages.

If you use one a lot – say every other day or even more – and you turn it up to a high heat level and speed, the chances are your hair will become dried out. I know this happens with mine. I use my drier regularly and think all is fine, then one day my hair no longer looks shiny and healthy, instead it has become brittle and dull. When this happens, I know it's time for a good conditioning treatment and to have a period of drying my hair naturally.

Natural drying is, in fact, the best way. If you have the time, let your hair hang loose and leave it to dry. If your hair comes out frizzy or very flat when left to dry in this way, then use your blow drier only to set it in place: with just a few 'blasts' and a circular brush, you can still achieve the coiffured look.

Of course, it's not always possible to dry your hair naturally, particularly during the winter months, so when using your hairdryer always ensure you don't pull the hair around the brush too tightly and use the dryer for as short a time as possible on a medium setting. Hairdressers now use a 'diffuser'. This is attached to the hairdryer and diffuses the hot air onto a larger area so avoiding the concentrated flow of hot air onto a small section of the hair.

I can remember when heated rollers first became popular during my modelling days. Suddenly all the models who had become well known for their sleek bobs and long straight hair, were appearing curled up to the nines. Heated rollers are the most effective way of curling hair. They are a lot less effort than curling tongs and certainly less painful than sleeping in rollers. There are two kinds: those with dry heat and those with a moisturizing steam. The latter are better if you are going to use them regularly, but be warned that heated rollers can and do dry out hair.

My advice is to let your hair dry before you put in the rollers. Then if your hair is difficult to set, use a small amount of gel or setting lotion (flat beer is a very effective setting lotion) on the hair and allow the heat of the rollers to dry it. Then remove the rollers, and gently brush your hair out.

Obviously, the kind of hair you have will dictate how curly it looks. Very thick hair usually falls quickly, the curls become quite loose and may even end up as just a wave. With fine hair, you will probably get a pronounced curl and need to be careful not to overdo it.

For side curls and curling a fringe, curling tongs and heated combs are a great idea. They do the job easily and effectively. If I am going out to dinner after a show, I sometimes use the curling tongs to curl the side strands and make them really cork-screwish. Then I pile the rest of my uncurled hair on top of my head or tie it into a tight knot at the back.

Another way of curling hair is to comb a glob of foam through the hair. Then roughly dry the hair upside down – this adds volume to it. When it is semi-dry, section off portions and pin-curl them. Or wind the portion round your fingers and pin down. Spray with a light setting lotion and leave until dry. Then remove the pins and comb through your hair with the fingers or a large-toothed comb. Don't brush the hair as it may become frizzy.

Colouring Your Hair

There is something quite thrilling in being able to alter dramatically your appearance by changing your hair colour. It always evokes a reaction – although maybe not always favourable! A friend who had rather pretty ash-blonde hair used to moan a lot because she didn't think it exciting enough. Then one day she turned up with her long, straight blonde hair cut into layers, bushed out and dyed jet black! She certainly looked different, and although I preferred her natural look there's no doubt she gained enormous pleasure from the change.

Most of us have hair which Nature designed to complement our eyes and skin colour so this must be taken into account if you are planning a change. I know one girl who spent weeks looking at pictures of redheads, commenting on how beautiful their hair was. She would remark upon people in the street with red hair, and it was quite clear she was very tempted to give it a try herself. Fortunately, she had the sense to use a semi-permanent colour and dyed her light brown hair a vivid auburn. The colour itself was lovely but it made her skin, which has a lot of red in it, look very florid and just didn't work with her light blue eyes. She realized this too and spent about a month with her head wrapped up in a turban until the colour had more or less washed out. Whereas another friend with dark brown hair used natural henna, available in various shades now, to give a bright red sheen to her hair and the effect was marvellous.

It really is important to have a hard look at yourself before selecting a new shade of hair colour. If possible, try on a wig in the colour you are considering, or put on a scarf or sweater in the shade and see what it does for you.

The swatches of colour which appear alongside home-colouring kits in most shops give an indication of what to expect, but you must remember that the swatches usually start out white, so do allow for the actual shade being duller and slightly darker. This is why most manufacturers advise you to test the colour on a small piece of your hair before you coat the lot.

I began colouring my hair in my teens while still at school. I have vivid memories of buying bottles of bleach and crude hair-colouring kits from chain-stores, and my hair got into a pretty grim condition as a result. This is the risk you take if you try doing too much to your hair. These days I'm more cautious. I stick to highlights, which work particularly well with my long hair. But I do enjoy the more extreme things other people do. I thought the punk and post-punk hair-styles in all their crazy colours were spectacular. It was as though someone had taken a high-quality box of the brightest possible paints on to the streets and painted the heads! Although I have had a reputation for being slightly loony and very fashionable, I've never really done anything that bizarre or zany. But I admire those who do, and cannot understand people who disapprove of these extreme looks. I think it takes a particular kind of bravado and courage – and certainly makes life more interesting!

There are many different ways in which to colour hair these days and a great deal of work has gone into improving the products used to do it. Even so, it is worth bearing in mind the point made by the American Science Action Coalition group, who have researched hair products: they say that all chemicals can cause allergy and scalp problems, bleaches carrying less risk of this than colour dyes.

Products which alter hair colour divide into different categories:

Bleaching

Jean Harlow used peroxide to bleach her hair to a bright, light blonde and created the fashion for this kind of hair colourant. She probably also encouraged a great many women to do immeasurable harm to their tresses.

Peroxide strips out the colour from the hair by destroying the pigment. Using it on its own is not a good idea because it acts slowly which means that the product must stay a long time on the hair, weakening it all the time. Use instead bleaches which contain peroxide because these usually also contain ammonia which speeds up the process considerably. Carefully-formulated bleaches should also consist of a conditioner which reduces the drying effects of the lightening process. A study done in America has shown that bleaches with protein leave hair less brittle and stronger than other products, so it is worth looking out for these.

Bleach is used in a variety of ways. It can be applied to the whole head or to small sections of hair to create highlights. Most of us think of bleach as a way to make hair blonde but it can also be used simply to lift natural colour a few shades. For example, someone with very dark brown hair could use bleach to lighten their hair to a reddish-auburn; it can be very effective in lifting mousey-brown hair a shade or two to a dark ash-blonde. I know someone who completely transformed her appearance in this way. Her hair had never been a feature of her looks and she always came across as a rather subdued-looking person. Then she bleached her hair to dark blonde; she left the bleach on a little longer around the hairline, which resulted in very fair curly bits acting almost as a halo to her face. The effect was stunning and it encouraged her to try a quite dramatic make-up too.

There are many different shades of blonde hair and very often your hairdresser will first strip the hair with a bleach, then use a toner rinse on top to create the desired shade. For example, it is very difficult to achieve a subtle silver-blonde by just using bleach so a rinse is applied to tone down the yellow-gold shade created by the removal of the pigment. If you want a whole head of blonde hair, do remember how important conditioning is. I am sure we have all seen heads of hair intended to make their owners looks like Hollywood vamps but which in fact, to the dispassionate observer, look like bales of hay!

There are plenty of products on the market for bleaching your own hair, but a proper blonding job requires a great deal of care. If you only want to go a couple of shades lighter, then try a hair lightener which is combed through the hair and left for about half an hour. That is relatively simple to apply, but it is a lot harder to use the thick bleach required for complete stripping of the natural colour, and if you happen to miss a piece of hair when applying it or you don't get right down to the roots you will end up looking a bit like a piebald pony! I would advise always going to a hairdresser for this.

Highlights

Highlights have become one of the most popular ways of lightening hair, and because only a small amount of the hair is lightened this method is far less damaging to the hair.

My natural hair colour is quite a dark brown-blonde shade. I have had highlights for years because I think a lighter colour goes well with my colouring but I would not consider an all-over bleach – particularly with long hair. In fact, I think highlights generally look better than solid bleached blonde. They give a lovely, subtle, tawny effect, mixed with the natural hair colour.

It is important to have highlights put in by a hairdresser who will do them very carefully. Otherwise you may end up with great hunks of bleached hair lying alongside hunks of natural hair, which looks most unattractive. The idea is for the lightened sections to blend in with your natural hair. One method, a speciality of Daniel Galvin, is weaving: a few strands of hair are lifted in between your own hair and bleached; they then fall quite naturally into your head of hair.

I just have the roots of my highlights done every couple of months. Some hairdressers run the bleach through the hair every time it is highlighted, but the risk here is that the hair will become over-bleached and will split. This method is fine if your hair is cut regularly but it is not a good idea if you are growing it.

I have blonde highlights, all the same colour, but another very effective style is the tortoiseshell look: sections of hair are bleached to several different shades of blonde and reddish-blonde, to create a very pretty, natural effect. Reverse highlights have also become popular in which sections of hair are dyed to contrast with your natural colour and with any bleached highlights.

Permanent colour

These contain peroxide and work by stripping the hair's natural colour and 'filling in' with their own shade. They can make hair a good deal lighter than its natural shade. The colour will fade in due course but generally it remains until you need to touch up the roots.

Semi-Permanent Colours

These are usually applied like shampoos. They are left on the hair for about twenty minutes for the colour to develop, then rinsed off. Many products for home use include a special after-treatment shampoo. Semi-permanent colours work by penetrating the hair shaft and enriching the natural colour. They gradually fade after about eight shampoos and need re-doing.

Temporary Rinses

These are ideal if you want to try a new shade and are not after something much lighter and brighter than your natural colour. Rinses are applied after your hair is shampooed and they coat the hair shaft without affecting it permanently. They wash off at the next shampoo.

Colouring Your Hair at Home

Many products can be used at home. The temporary rinses and semi-permanent rinses, for example, are very simple to use. Permanent dyes, however, are probably better applied by a hairdresser who will know which brand is best for your hair. He or she will gauge how porous your hair is and therefore how long the colour should be left on and how much conditioning is needed afterwards. Like bleaching, this kind of dyeing is fairly violent to the hair, so extreme care is needed.

Perming Your Hair

The ancient Egyptians devised the idea of forming the hair into shapes by plastering mud and water on the hair and leaving it to dry. I can only say I am glad science has moved on from that idea!

Many of the Thirties and Forties Hollywood stars had perms and in those days it was done by winding the hair around rods wrapped in cloth, then coating it in perming lotion. Today perms are a way of life. They are used by so many people in so many different ways. The soft, bouncy perms done on big rollers are ideal for putting body and bounce into limp hair. Thick hair permed on medium-sized rollers comes out in a glorious mane of curls. Perms can give a wave to long hair and they can be used to style short cuts into wonderful shapes.

Perms work by changing the way the hair grows, by re-shaping it into a curl. Lotion is applied to the hair which is then curled around the rollers – small for a tight curl, large for loose – then once the hair is re-shaped the rollers are removed, the lotion washed off and the new shape is set with neutralizing liquid.

Thank goodness perms don't damage hair in the way they did twenty years ago. Today, the perming lotions have been refined to reduce the damage done to hair. It is an unavoidable fact, however, that a perm will dry your hair – a bonus if you have very greasy hair, of course – and it may put it out of condition for a little while, but if you have it done professionally and you are diligent about conditioning your permed hair, you should not have any problems. It is sensible to condition your hair well both before your appointment as well as afterwards.

Before deciding to see what the curled looked does for you, make sure you are in good health. If you have a virus, are run down or sickening for something, this affects your hair and so the results will be poor.

Don't perm newly-coloured hair. In fact, it is unwise to perm hair which is tinted, dyed or bleached all over, as the joint effect

Having your hair done can be fun, or a drag – pleasurable or uncomfortable – depending on how you're feeling and what's happening. I think I enjoyed this session!

Debbie was backbrushing my hair section by section and spraying it to get the really wild party look to go with the fuchsia-coloured two-piece.

A softer, less dishevelled look. Debbie used foam mousse and
Molton Browners, then put me under the dryer for twenty minutes before
a careful comb-out.

is very drying and may make the hair break. But if you are determined to do both, have your perm a few weeks after your colouring session, or have highlights rather than a total colour.

Try to avoid having a perm on top of hair which is already permed. Have it cut before your new perm so that at least the ends are removed. But if you do perm over an old perm, use very gentle lotion indeed.

You can perm your hair at home but, frankly, I don't advise it. Perming is not particularly easy; a trained hairdresser can tell when the curl is 'set', something you may not be able to yourself. Nor will you necessarily be able to see whether or not the perm is taking.

Other Hair Products

Gels   These are used for sculpting and shaping the hair by combing through wet or dry hair. You can create a 'wet' look on dry hair for a dramatic style. Punk styles need lots of gel. It gives a rather hard feel to the hair when it dries but can be brushed or washed out easily. Gives extra body and makes hair easier to style when used on wet hair.

Mousses   These give body and shine and make hair easier to style. Use a golfball-size glob in the palm of the hand and smooth' all over hair, then either comb or scrunch hair depending on the desired outcome. They can be used with or without a hairdryer. They are also good for controlling fly-away, static hair, although not as strong as a gel. They leave hair soft, not stiff. They can be used on dry hair to smooth hair down and help when putting hair up in a more glamorous, formal style. Use on sides of hair for a sleek appearance.

For a quick pick-me-up for your hairstyle the next day: spray your hair with water and the foam mousse will spring back to life.

D I E T

I WAS a teenage junk food addict! Hamburgers, cream buns, ice-cream whips, you name it, I devoured the lot. And, of course in those days nobody thought much about eating for health. People worried only about which foods were most fattening and as I was lucky enough not to have to watch my weight, I could eat exactly as I wished. I take what I eat far more seriously now. Not that I can remember ever feeling unwell on the food I used to eat, but I am sure it wouldn't suit the kind of active, busy life-style I have developed over recent years – combining the strenuous demands of working in shows with motherhood and the running of a home – particularly as I am no longer a teenager with the kind of endless energy teenagers so often seem to have.

It is important to understand how and why food affects our bodies. It is part of growing up to care for ourself. After all, food is our life-blood – literally. What we eat affects every single bit of us. So the quality of our food is all-important. If I am going to lead a life that requires a lot of stamina and energy, then I need to be certain that the fuel I give my body is the best possible. So these days I aim to have balanced meals – not a sandwich or a bun grabbed in between a busy set of engagements as I have done in the past. Frankly, I can't afford to be unwell. And that applies to most women today, who work hard and have families. There just isn't time to be ill! Although you many not actually fall ill from eating too much junk food, you will almost certainly feel a lot less healthy than if you follow a nutritious, balanced diet.

The emphasis today is on eating the right foods to stay healthy. Whether the food is fattening or not is almost a secondary concern, which I consider a good development. I have friends, for instance, of a large build, but they are fit, they have firm bodies and so they look good. There are other large people I know who take virtually no exercise, and therefore tend to look flabby; their posture is bad too, so that one is very aware of their being overweight.

However, a healthy diet can also be slimming. High fibre foods, for example, are generally more filling than refined foods; and cutting down on fatty foods and sugar will certainly help you to lose weight.

But although I feel strongly about eating the correct foods – and as a mother I consider it my responsibility to be sure my daughter has a balanced diet – I am not a fanatic. I loathe fanaticism. In many books good health is presented almost as an endurance test, in which you must suffer to achieve it. But eating well does not involve suffering; it does, however, require a bit of thought and it may take some getting used to if you regularly eat junk food. I certainly had to wean myself off too many hamburgers, although I still enjoy them and treat myself occasionally for I don't believe that the odd indulgence will wreck the good a sensible food programme can do.

So much has been written about eating over the past few years that many people have become utterly confused about what is and is not good for us; it seems that every other week a new 'wonder' food is found or a scientific discovery about nutrition is made. The sensible thing is to look at the thoughts on nutrition and diet which have been around for a while now and which seem to be widely approved of, and try to incorporate these into your life.

NUTRITION

BASICALLY, the body needs nutrients to nourish the cells. It has been said that we need forty different nutrients, but for most of us that gets too complicated and it would be too much to try to remember them all. Instead, why not learn the different categories of nutrients and what foods go to make up each category. The nutrient categories are: protein, carbohydrates, fats, vitamins, minerals, fibre and water. We need all of these and we need them combined in our diet at the same time.

Protein

Our bodies are largely made up of protein, which is broken down into twenty-two different forms of amino acid. These replenish body tissue, our hair, nails, hormones, and they renew cells. It is also worth knowing, if you lead a physically active life as I do, that muscles contain more protein than any other part of the body and if your diet contains too little protein, your muscles may lose their elasticity. On the other hand, too much protein can put a strain on the kidneys and any excess which does not get burnt up is stored in the body as fat. Clearly, therefore, we must try to eat just the amount our body needs and can cope with.

There are no hard and fast rules about how much protein we should eat every day, but it is widely agreed that the old idea of a large portion of protein for every meal is unnecessary. If you have a normal-sized portion of chicken, meat or fish, or an egg a

Vitamins have been held up as 'miracle' cures for all sorts of illnesses, from common colds to cancer. I don't know how to react to these claims. I'm all in favour of natural medicine whenever possible, but I can't help feeling that in some cases there may be more faith than scientific fact.

That said, I do think it's worth taking Vitamin C if you feel a cold coming on. This idea was put forward by Dr Linus Pauling who has done a lot of work with Vitamin C and I, in company with plenty of people I know, find that taking a large dose whenever I feel a cold developing, prevents it from actually happening. Dr Pauling recommends taking three grams of Vitamin C three times a day for three days.

Many claims have been made for Vitamin E, ranging from it improving your sex life to it preventing ageing, healing wounds and relieving menstrual pains. It is widely recommended by nutritionists. I have listed below the different vitamins, the claims made for them and the various foods in which they are found. You can then work out exactly what your needs are.

VITAMIN A Keeps skin healthy, soft and smooth. Helps in the repair of tissues and mucous membranes. Essential for seeing in poor light – a deficiency could lead to night blindness.
Available in cod-liver oil and halibut liver capsules, oil-rich fish, kidneys, liver, carrots, greens and butter.

VITAMIN B Not a single vitamin but a complex made up of several different substances including thiamine B1, riboflavin B2, niacin B3. Essential to the nervous system, for making new blood cells and other body cells. A deficiency can cause anaemia, lack of sleep, irritability and stress, dry hair and dry skin.
Available in brewer's yeast tablets, liver, wheatgerm and milk.

(Opposite) **Vitamin A helps to keep my skin healthy, soft and smooth. If particular vitamins are contained in foods you dislike, you can always take them as a pill or capsule.**

VITAMIN C   Needed to form connective tissue fibres –
essential therefore to all organs in the body
except the nervous system. Helps to heal sores,
wounds, pulled ligaments etc. Many people say
that taking large doses can help to prevent
colds and 'flu. Smoking impairs the body's
ability to absorb Vitamin C, so smokers should
take extra doses.
*Available in all fruits and vegetables – particularly
oranges – rose-hips and paprika.*

VITAMIN D   Necessary for the formation of healthy bones
and teeth since it promotes the penetration of
calcium and phosphorous which form them.
Can be obtained when sunlight reacts with an
inert substance in the skin (ergosterol) and
converts it into calciferol.
Available in cod-liver oil, butter, eggs and fatty fish.

VITAMIN E   Helps in the healing of scar tissue, cuts and
burns. Now often used in skin creams,
especially those for dry skins. Women suffering
from pre-mentrual tension and menstrual pain
sometimes find that taking measured doses can
alleviate the problems.
Available in nuts, eggs and wholewheat bread.

VITAMIN F   Needed for the flow of oxygen from the blood
stream into the tissues and organs. A deficiency
can cause dandruff, dull hair and poor skin.
Available in vegetable oils and wheatgerm.

VITAMIN K   Necessary for the formation of thrombin, the
enzyme which aids blood-clotting.
Available in green vegetables.

Remember that over-cooking destroys the natural vitamins in foods. Always steam vegetables; never boil them in a pan full of water because in that way you lose all the goodness. For example, by boiling cabbage in a saucepan of cold water, you lose 75 per cent of the natural nutrients. A simple and sensible solution is to invest in a steamer or pressure cooker, where the vegetables are cooked in just a tiny amount of water, so as to preserve the natural vitamins.

Deep frying is disastrous for food – as well as for your complexion and figure: all the nutrients go into the fat which you then discard. (It would be even worse if you were to eat it!) So avoid fried foods and grill instead.

Minerals

Minerals are a bit like the wallflower at a party. They don't seem to merit the same attention as other nutrients. But minerals are in fact absolutely vital to our health. They affect just about every organism, from soft tissue, bones, muscles, the heart, to the functioning of the brain, the nerves and the production of hormones – so you can see how important they are.

Mineral deficiency affects the body in a variety of ways: it can cause hair and skin problems, pre-menstrual tension and mild depression, and there is an even greater risk of these problems if you have a refined diet.

The main minerals are contained in many of the foods we eat: milk, for example, is a good source of calcium; many seeds, nuts and whole grains contain magnesium; phosphorus is found in milk products and unrefined foods, and potassium is in unrefined grains, fruits and vegetables.

We obtain trace vitamins, also important, by a more remote process. These come from the ground in which food is grown, or they are found in the sea and so can be eaten in seafood. Sadly, as so many chemicals are now used to grow fruit and vegetables, many of the trace elements are now depleted, which is why it is worth buying organically-grown produce where no chemicals are used. These do tend, however, to be more expensive and are often difficult to find. It's sensible, therefore, to grow your own fruit and vegetables if you can.

Fibre

Fibre is the most fashionable of the food ingredients and with the health boom in recent years, it has become the ingredient pinpointed as all-important but too often missing from our diet. Fibre – the coating of grains found in their natural state – contains precious minerals and vitamins. But when foods are refined they lose this important coating. The post-war fashion for creating pristine foods meant that almost all the grain carbohydrates were processed and bleached with such ferocity that they were stripped of every gram of fibre. The irony is that now, due to the growing interest in health foods, instead of leaving foods unrefined, manufacturers have continued the stripping process – but boast on the packets of all the fibre and vitamins they have added afterwards!

You might think what does it matter if we eat refined foods, provided we take vitamin and mineral supplements to replace the lost qualities of fibre? Well, aside from being silly to pay out money for vitamins and minerals which can be had naturally in your food, there are other reasons why fibre is important. Fibre, or roughage as it is inelegantly known, encourages bowel action by speeding the removal of waste from the intestine. Over the years, since food-refining first became popular, doctors have noted a dramatic increase in gut illness, digestive problems and degenerative disease. Bowel cancer has also been linked to a lack of fibre, so it seems thoroughly good sense to me to ensure you get an adequate amount of fibre from your food.

Brown bread is one of the commonest foods to contain fibre. But do be careful that you buy the right brown bread. A lot of bread which appears to be brown is in fact made from white flour which has been dyed brown (white flour is used so as to retain in the loaf the puffy consistency which comes with refined flour) in order to satisfy the popular demand for brown bread. Ask whether your bread is genuine wholegrain, or find a baker where you know they bake with real brown flour.

But, having said all this, I have to admit there *are* times when I long for a French baguette – the long white loaf – or a plateful of white spaghetti, or perhaps some white scones. I allow myself these as a treat only very occasionally!

Water It is too easy to take water for granted, but it really is a vital part of our diet. In fact, we can live longer without food than we can without water. Our bodies are made up of 70 per cent water which is responsible for the functioning of our cells; it flushes waste products from the system, de-toxifies the body and acts as a solvent for the nutrients we take in. It also aids digestion and is said to be good for the complexion.

Nutritionists recommend we drink at least four pints of water a day. But don't necessarily rush to the nearest tap for those four pints because unfortunately, domestic water contains chemicals such as chlorine which are necessary to kill off germs. Sadly, this means that most domestic supplies of water are not actually very good for us in the end. So unless you live in a small rural area where your tap water comes from a pure, local source, it is worth investing in a tap water filter or buying bottled water.

Water filters are sold in many health shops now. They kill off the chemicals in tap water but at the same time allow the minerals through. Every so often you have to renew the filter cylinder which processes the water, but if you buy one with its own jug, it's very simple to do.

Another way of ensuring you drink chemical-free water, and one which has grown enormously in popularity over recent years, is to buy bottled water. There are a variety of different types of bottled water on the market. The poshest come from natural springs in France, although increasingly waters from other countries are being bottled, from Scotland for example. The advantage of many of these waters is that they contain minerals (check on the bottle label) without any of the pollutants.

Always important to drink plenty of non-alcoholic fluids and not only in a hot climate. Just hot water with lemon is delicious.

Bottled waters have quite different tastes and it is worth sampling a variety to see which you like best. You have a choice of still water and the bubbly carbonated kind. I prefer still water for drinking in quantity and with meals, but sometimes when drinking socially I find a glass of carbonated water with a slice of lemon is quite delicious in place of alcohol. In fact, try mixing mineral water with white wine if you don't want to drink too much or become too tiddly! Alcohol dehydrates the body which is why you get a hangover afterwards; drinking water helps to prevent that happening.

Contrary to popular belief, soft water is not better for you than hard water. In fact, quite the reverse may be true. Although soft water feels pleasant when washing hair and leaves the hands feeling softer after washing, it contains considerably less calcium and magnesium than hard water. And as these minerals are said to reduce the body's levels of lead, hard water would seem to be better for you.

Another effective way to use water is as part of a fast. Drinking only water for twenty-four hours or even longer is a thoroughly good way to de-toxify and cleanse the body, but do be sure to check with your doctor first. Opposite you will find information on fasting.

Salt Most of us have grown up expecting to find salt and pepper on the table, and our palates have come to assume that most foods need salt. However, evidence has shown that too much salt is bad for us: it can cause water retention in the body; it can put strain on the kidneys; it has been blamed for increasing the risk of heart disease, and can cause high blood pressure. Recent British reports state very firmly that we would be a great deal healthier if we ate a quarter of the amount of salt presently consumed. And I assume the figure would be much the same in America where food is just as heavily salted.

So how do we cut down on salt? The best way, of course, is just to stop putting it automatically on the table at every meal. Although at first your food will probably taste a little bland if you are used to a lot, in time you will adapt to the much subtler flavour of unsalted food. Good substitutes are also available. For example, tamari, a soya bean extract, is sold in health shops. Although this has a salty flavour, it is not composed of sodium and chloride as salt is. It is worth asking, too, in your local health shop for other alternatives – new salt substitutes are forever being introduced.

Cutting out salt as a seasoning is not much use, of course if you then load it into your cooking. Most of us do this quite automatically, and almost every recipe includes salt in its list of ingredients. Try reducing the amount by half. You probably won't notice a great deal of difference, and eventually you may find that most food tastes all right without any. Not all foods, however, are appetizing with *no* salt, but we overdo it most of the time, and it really is worthwhile training the palate to get used to eating less.

Always check the ingredients of prepared foods. You will find that most tins and packets contain salt, so try and avoid these. There are other good reasons for avoiding too many prepared foods: they tend to be processed, and any nutrients they do have are lost in the cooking. I'm horrified, too, at the number of additives in these prepared foods. We all use such foods, I know, for convenience occasionally – but that's exactly how I think they should be used – as just the occasional convenience and certainly not as part of our everyday diet.

FASTING

EVERY once in a while, I enjoy an outrageously, unhealthy binge of rich, fattening, self-indulgent foods. I wonder who doesn't? Sometimes, though, it is forced upon me. If, for example, I am invited out to a gala dinner or some such event, it would be extremely rude to refuse to eat the carefully prepared meal. But once I have had my binge I do need to do something to restore my body's health, to give it a clean out – and the best thing for this is a fast.

Some people fast for days – weeks even – and far from being wrecks at the end they seem to emerge feeling wonderfully fit and exhilarated. However, it would be foolish to try a long, hard fast without first consulting your doctor. If he gives you the go-ahead you should either go to a centre where fasting is practised regularly or seek the advice of someone who is experienced at fasting.

It is unwise to attempt a serious fast while being involved in any strenuous activity or if you are under stress. People who regard fasting as a serious part of their lives carry it out in very quiet, tranquil surroundings. But for a short fast of just a day or two – the kind I go in for – you don't need to bury yourself in a Tibetan monastery or a Scottish ashram! Plan a day which you know is going to be fairly peaceful, when you will have time to yourself to enjoy a long warm bath, to take a stroll in the countryside, or to relax with a good book. In other words, choose a time which is your own when you can pamper yourself.

I wouldn't, for example, fast on a day of shows which involved several hours' dancing. It would weaken me, and possibly be harmful. But if I have a couple of free days, then I'm quite happy to live purely on bottled water or fruit juice. Or another idea is to eat only fruit. The point of this is to give your digestive system and all the parts of your body involved in processing what you eat, a rest. It also means that the body can rid itself of the toxins which build up as we constantly process our food. By fasting, you eliminate the stored toxins through your kidneys. Fatty tissue then gets broken down and is used as energy – because there is no food to be used – which enables you to lose weight.

The initial stages of a fast can be a bit off-putting. As the body burns up the toxic substances, your tongue may go yellow and feel furry. Your breath will probably smell, and you may feel dizzy and develop a headache. The natural reaction is to think something has gone very wrong and to go straight out and eat a square meal. But avoid this panic reaction. These symptoms are actually a good sign – a sign that the body is getting rid of its waste matters – and they should pass fairly quickly.

A Twenty-Four Hour Fast

Here is a pleasant way to fast for twenty-four hours. If you are in good health it can only be beneficial. However, as I mentioned before, it is always sensible to check with a doctor before attempting any sort of fast.

Use only filtered or bottled water. There is no point in drinking water full of chemicals if you want to cleanse your system. Begin the day with a one-pint mug of warm water with a squirt of fresh lemon or orange. Alternatively, drink a mug of chilled water with a slice of lemon. You will probably feel hungry at meal-times, so when this happens drink another pint of water. If plain water is not interesting enough to maintain your willpower, add a dash of unsweetened apple or grape juice.

Basically, this is your 'menu' for the day. You can drink as much as you like but as far as possible stick to plain water as this is the best form of cleansing there is. When the hunger pangs are really bad – and they probably will be at times – you may have a cup of hot herbal tea. The warmth will take the edge off your appetite. But don't drink ordinary tea as this contains caffeine.

I suggest going for a swim, a walk or a gentle work-out in the early evening. (Don't do this if you feel faint! Perhaps first-time fasters should take a companion.) The exercise will leave you feeling relaxed. Then go home, hole up with a large cup of herbal tea and either watch a good movie on the television or read a book. Aim to get to bed early.

You should feel much healthier after your day's fast. If you feel up to it, add another twenty-four-hour stint which will give the body an even greater chance to cleanse itself.

THREE-DAY EATING PLAN

CELIA Wright, one of the directors of the Green Farm Nutrition Centre in Sussex, England, gave us this diet which is very beneficial. It will clear the system, cleanse the skin and provide you with energy.

Day One

This day is a fruit or vegetable fast which will help to expel toxins from skin and tissues. If you wish to prolong the diet, you can repeat day one for up to three days, and so derive maximum benefit.

Breakfast – Either (i) half a pound of grapes. *Or* (ii) one pint of carrot and celery juice, using a juice extractor. (Buy bottled juice if you are unable to make your own.) If you feel hunger pangs, eat sticks of carrot throughout the day.

Lunch – Either (i) apple and pear salad. If you prefer, eat the fruit whole. You can eat as much as you like of these fruits – snack throughout the afternoon if you wish. *Or* (ii) carrot and celery juice for breakfast, accompanied by celery sticks. Continue eating celery throughout the afternoon if you wish.

Dinner – Either (i) one whole pineapple. Slice, then serve decoratively. *Or* (ii) large vegetable salad using only fresh raw vegetables, dressed with virgin olive oil and fresh lemon juice.

Drink as much bottled water as you wish throughout the day.

Days Two and Three

On these days you start to rebuild your diet with high energy foods. You can safely eat this way indefinitely and besides gaining vitality, would lose weight too. Throughout each day you may drink weak tea (Indian or Chinese) with lemon rather than, milk, herbal tea, fruit and vegetable juices and bottled spring water.

Breakfast – *Either* (i) bowl of sugar-free muesli with five ounces of natural yoghurt plus a chopped or creamed banana with a sprinkling of sunflower or pumpkin seeds. *Or* (ii) cup of rolled oats, barley flakes and millet flakes cooked gently with two cups of water for five minutes. Serve with a chopped banana or some dried fruit, and five ounces of natural yoghurt.

Lunch – *Either* (i) large raw vegetable salad as for dinner on Day One, this time with a baked potato and a little cottage, goat's or sheep's cheese. (Some people are allergic to cow's milk products, which may make them feel unwell, cause weight gain and skin problems. Goat's milk or soya milk and their products should then be used.) *Or* (ii) raw vegetable sticks with a portion of houmus, made from chick peas, or taramassalata made from cod's roe (both can be bought in many delicatessens and supermarkets). Or if you prefer, have curd cheese.

Dinner – *Either* (i) cup of brown rice, washed and then simmered in two cups of water. Add one cup of finely sliced vegetables as the water-line goes below the rice. Replace the lid and allow to steam, stirring occasionally. Serve with a little soy sauce. *Or* (ii) average portion of white fish, gently grilled or baked for twenty mintes. Serve with a raw vegetable salad, one steamed vegetable (courgettes, broccoli etc.) and a baked potato. Add olive oil, lemon juice and a little soy sauce if you wish.
(NB. Soy sauce contains salt, so use sparingly in both of these dishes.)

On completing the twenty-four hour fast or three-day diet you will feel much better, and will probably be determined to try to eat healthily in future. Finding wholefoods – foods that are not full of additives and salt – is not difficult. Health food shops can now be found in most high streets – even small towns have caught on to the fact that people are interested in good quality foods. Health food shops stock a range of wholefood cereals, pastas, rice, flour, natural yoghurt, tahini, dried fruits, nuts, seeds, grain, and pulses such as kidney beans, chick peas or lentils. Many large supermarkets, too, stock brown flour, pastas, rice and pulses.

THIS is a good, sensible seven-day diet recommended by the Vegetarian Society. It doesn't promise sudden weight loss but you should lose about 2 lbs in the week. It is based on an intake of approximately 1,000 calories a day, in addition to which you can drink a quarter of a pint of whole milk or half a pint of skimmed milk. Drink lots of mineral water as well. Obviously you can switch these foods around and replace suggested foods with others so long as they have approximately the same calorie content. Don't cook vegetables too long or you will lose all the vitamins and minerals, and keep the water they are cooked in for soup stock.

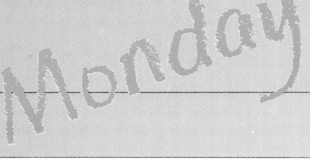

ONE THOUSAND CALORIES A DAY DIET

DAY 1

		No. of calories
Breakfast:	½ grapefruit	30
	poached egg	90
	2 slices wholewheat toast/bread	150
	1 teaspoon butter or vegetable margarine	50
		—
		320
Lunch:	110g/4oz low fat cottage cheese with herbs	120
	50g grated carrot	20
	green salad with light French dressing	62
	2 crispbreads and 1 teaspoon butter or margarine	106
		—
		308
Dinner:	Orange segments and 6 grapes	65
	110g/4oz French beans, steamed	12
	25g/1oz toasted almonds	170
	2 tablespoons brown rice	45
		—
		292

Tuesday

Day 2

Breakfast:	150g/5oz fat-free yoghurt	5
	1 teaspoon bran	18
	1 dessertspoon seedless raisins	48
	1 orange or small apple	50
	1 crispbread	28
		___
		264

Lunch:	1 cup clear vegetable soup with herbs	30
	green salad	30
	1 hard-boiled egg	90
	1 slice wholewheat bread	75
	1 teaspoon butter or vegetable margarine	50
		___
		275

Dinner:	½ grapefruit with chopped mint	32
	ratatouille	140
	25g/1oz cheese	120
	1 grated apple	50
	1 tablespoons yoghurt	30
		___
		372

Day 3

Breakfast:	2 dessertspoons muesli	80
	4 soaked prunes with juice	48
	110g/4oz skimmed milk or yoghurt	55
	110g/4oz fresh milk	50
		233

Lunch:	watercress	5
	2 small grated carrots	20
	1 tomato, 1 stick celery	15
	½ small green pepper	12
	40g/1½ cheese	180
	2 crispbreads	56
	1 teaspoon butter or vegetable margarine	50
		338

Dinner:	50g/2oz haricot or black-eyed beans cooked with	
	110g/4oz of onion and 1 tomato	180
	1 small jacket potato	60
	110g/4oz spring greens	20
	orange and date salad (1 orange, 4 dates)	95
		355

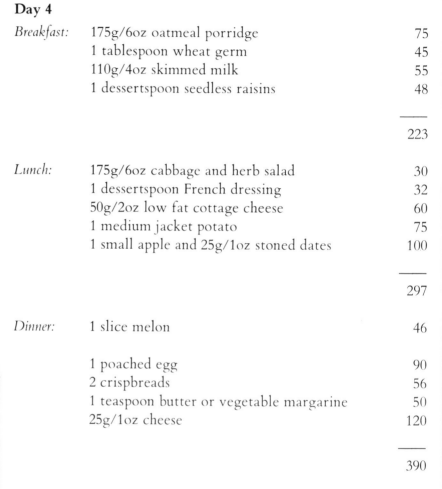

Day 4

Breakfast:	175g/6oz oatmeal porridge	75
	1 tablespoon wheat germ	45
	110g/4oz skimmed milk	55
	1 dessertspoon seedless raisins	48
		223
Lunch:	175g/6oz cabbage and herb salad	30
	1 dessertspoon French dressing	32
	50g/2oz low fat cottage cheese	60
	1 medium jacket potato	75
	1 small apple and 25g/1oz stoned dates	100
		297
Dinner:	1 slice melon	46
	1 poached egg	90
	2 crispbreads	56
	1 teaspoon butter or vegetable margarine	50
	25g/1oz cheese	120
		390

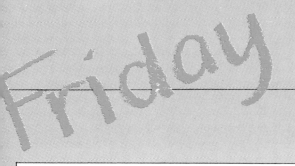
Day 5

Breakfast:	1 tablespoon soaked apricots	35
	2 tablespoons yoghurt	55
	1 tablespoon bran	18
	1 dessertspoon wholewheat flakes	40
	1 slice wholewheat toast/bread	75
	1 teaspoon butter or vegetable margarine	50
		273

Lunch:	75g/3oz root salad (carrot, celery or celeriac)	45
	green salad with French dressing	62
	25g/1oz almonds	170
	1 small portion fresh fruit	40
		317

Dinner:	75g/3oz vegeburger and mixed vegetables	235
	1 crispbread	28
	25g/1oz cottage cheese with herbs	30
	25g/3oz fresh fruit salad	45,
		338

Saturday

DAY 6

Breakfast:	1 medium apple, grated	45
	25g/1oz stoned dates	70
	50g/2oz whole milk	40
	2 crispbreads	56
	1 teaspoon butter or vegetable margarine	50
		—
		261

Lunch:	110g/4oz raw beetroot and apple salad with	
	chopped mint	60
	mustard and cress	5
	50g/2oz hazelnut 'marbles' (see recipe below)	150
	2 tablespoons yoghurt	55
		—
		270

Dinner:	1 cup lentil soup	80
	110g/4oz Brussel sprouts	20
	savoury baked custard (made with 1 egg and	
	25g/1oz cheese)	250
	1 medium pear	45
		—
		395

Hazel Nut Marbles

Chop a medium-sized onion (around 4 oz) finely, and cook gently with a crushed glove of garlic in a dessertspoon of oil. Add approximately 4oz ground hazel nuts, chopped fresh rosemary or other herb and yeast extract to taste, and enough vegetable stock to bind into marbles. Roll these in a few more ground nuts, and serve them cold.

Sunday

DAY 7

Breakfast:	3 tablespoons yoghurt	75
	1 small banana	45
	2 dessertspoon wholewheat flakes	40
	1 slice wholewheat toast	75
	1 teaspoon butter or vegetable margarine	50
		285
Lunch:	green mixed salad with dressing	52
	1 scrambled egg and 25g/1oz mushrooms	125
	1 small jacket potato	60
	1 orange	50
		287
Dinner:	½ grapefruit and chopped mint	35
	175g/6oz steamed cauliflower	30
	1½oz grated cheese	180
	1 tablespoon brown rice	28
	1 small baked apple	55
		328

Not a weight-reducing diet but a healthy seven-day diet to give you energy. Your intake each day is approximately two thousand calories.

Monday

Day 1

Breakfast
2 thick slices wholemeal toast each spread with
15g/½oz butter or margarine and
15g/½oz each marmalade
150ml/¼ pint fresh orange juice

Lunch
175g/6oz cooked pasta, preferably wholemeal, mixed with
75g/3oz cooked white fish,
50g/2oz prawns and
100ml/6 tablespoons cheese sauce

1 piece fresh fruit

Dinner
75g/3oz lean beef served as stew
1 large (225g/8oz) baked jacket potato
50g/2oz peas
75g/3oz carrots

small portion fruit crumble

Day 6

Breakfast
50g/2oz high-fibre breakfast cereal
200ml/⅓ pint semi-skimmed milk
50g/2oz chopped apricots

Lunch
300ml/½ pint soup with
1 wholemeal bread roll and 15g/½oz butter or margarine

1 pitta bread
75g/3oz houmus
2 raw tomatoes, celery and carrot sticks

Dinner
110g/4oz roast pork fillet stuffed with prunes
150g/5oz cooked red cabbage with onion and apple
175g/6oz cooked pasta or brown rice

small portion apple pie (single crust)
2 tablespoons 35% fat (whipping) cream

Sunday

Day 7

Breakfast
2 shredded wheat
150ml/¼ pint semi-skimmed milk
50g/2oz raisins or other dried fruit

Lunch
200g/7oz cauliflower with
75g/3oz boiled leeks and
110g/4oz cheese sauce
75g/3oz peas and carrots

1 wholemeal bread roll

200g/7oz baked apple with
15g/½oz sugar or syrup
25g/1oz raisins

Dinner
200g/7oz herring in oatmeal, grilled
110g/4oz mustard sauce
sliced green beans
broccoli or spinach

1 pear with chocolate sauce

Each day, select one of these snacks – more if you are very energetic:

2 glasses wine
3 digestive biscuits
small bar chocolate
3 portions fresh fruit
1 thick slice bread with 15g/½oz butter or margarine
25g/1oz Cheddar cheese and 1 portion fruit
25g/1oz nuts and 25g/1oz dried fruit
150g/5oz fruit yoghurt and 1 portion fresh fruit
300ml/½ pint semi-skimmed milk and 1 plain biscuit

D A N C E

THE night Ginger Rogers came to see me on Broadway in *My One and Only* and came backstage to tell me she had enjoyed it so much she'd wanted to get up on stage and join in, I felt I had really made the grade as a dancer.

It still seems unreal, almost like a fairy tale, that I should have had the chance to star in a New York Broadway musical. I had no interest in dancing as a child. I remember my mum taking me to classes once, but I took one look at all the other children – I was dreadfully shy – and just ran away! So that was that. My older sisters were the dancers. I can still remember them being photographed, wearing top hats and grass skirts.

Like so many people, I grew up thinking of dance as something which requires natural talent, that you need to be born with dancing feet. There's a lot of mystique attached to it – I suppose that because dance is described as one of the arts many people feel it belongs to a talented élite. Well, that's just not true of course and now that it has become such a popular form of exercise, much of the mystique surrounding it has vanished.

I didn't start dancing seriously until after my modelling career, although I do remember one occasion when I was due to do a commercial, and the director suddenly announced that it was to be a musical. It turned out that I had to come on dancing with some other girls. I was very scared – can you imagine being asked to perform a routine when you just don't know how to dance? But I got some hasty coaching and managed all right.

Up till then, I hadn't really thought of myself as a dancer, even though I had danced in *The Boy Friend*. But Tommy Tune made clear from the beginning that he had complete faith in me, and his support helped me enormously. If you are learning to dance and really want to develop it, it's important that you have a friend – or, if you have one, a partner – who takes an interest, encourages you, offers constructive criticism, and generally gives support. It does make a lot of difference. Tommy built up my confidence by talking of 'special quality'; he helped me to believe in myself.

Learning the starring role of Edith Herbert for *My One and Only*, in which I was on stage throughout most of the show, is one of the most difficult things I have ever done. And like most of the major events in my life, it happened quite unexpectedly. Tommy Tune, a terrific choreographer and theatrical director, and I had worked together in the past and had become firm friends. We'd talked occasionally about how we would like to dance together again – and then one day there was Tommy on the phone, calling me from America, to say that he was doing *My One and Only* and wanted me to partner him in it.

Well, of course I was thrilled, quite ecstatic. What an opportunity! But I bet the producers didn't feel that thrilled – I can imagine they had heart-failure when they first heard. After all, it wasn't as if I was a big acting name in the States at the time, even though I had done *The Boy Friend*.

I said yes immediately. Mind you, afterwards I did wonder what on earth I was doing. It was impulse, pure instinct that made me accept. And when I found out that I was to be on stage for practically the entire performance, well then I began to get cold feet – so to speak! There was I, faced with having to learn to dance this big part, with having to become good enough to cope with all the different tap-dance steps and routines – even one done with my feet under water – as well as learning a little bit of the Charleston for the beginning of the show! But it was like riding a bike – if you've once known how to do it, it will all come back.

Step, kick. Much harder work than it looks, but the secret is to make it look easy.

So, once I knew what was expected of me, I began tap and jazz classes – and, believe me, they were quite a shock to the system. However, I wasn't quite a beginner, starting from scratch. *The Boy Friend*, after all, had been ten years before, and the dancing in that had given me a good foundation. This time I had to perform live on stage, which is very, very different from film where the scenes are shot in small sequences and can be done again and again. But the fact that in really quite a short time I reached the required standard proves that it's possible for plenty of other people to learn to dance. I wasn't in any way exceptionally talented – I just worked extremely hard.

Karen Tamburelli, a really fabulous American dancer also in the show, gave me lessons. She broke down the dance steps for me and taught me exactly how to do each one. It was a wonderful education working with her. She had been tap dancing for a long time and, an experienced teacher, knew precisely how to show me the steps in slow motion. That's the kind of teacher you need if you are learning something as complicated as tap, which is fast and difficult to follow at full pace. Otherwise, it's all too easy to learn things incorrectly.

I was very nervous in the beginning. I lacked confidence and felt self-conscious. I kept looking at my feet to see if I was doing the right thing. And I still remember Karen continually telling me to relax and bend my legs which, of course, is the only way to tap dance. But like so many people, I found it hard to let myself go at first.

I learnt small sequences at a time, rehearsing them over and over until I really felt I knew what I was doing. Then I would move on to new steps. I think that's the best way to learn, rather than trying to memorize a long sequence all at once – the chances are you'll get some of it wrong and then it's very difficult to un-learn.

I found it hard-going at first. There I would be, struggling to get a sequence right, tense with nerves, and knowing all the time that on stage it had to look very relaxed, zappy and fun. And the only way to achieve that effect, of course, is to work and work on the routine.

I am very disciplined about my work. That's something I learnt from my early modelling days. A very ordinary kid like me certainly got a lucky break, but if I hadn't have worked hard and made something of it, then it could all have come to nothing. And that applies particularly to dance: if you want to be good, to make the most of your lessons, then it's essential to be dedicated and disciplined.

I didn't know if I could be the number one performer in the country, but I was going to give the best performance I was capable of doing. I rehearsed in the studio eight hours a day and then sometimes I would go home and put in extra time there. It certainly amused Carly. She even picked up quite a few of the steps and got to know the music well enough to sing some of the songs. But some nights by the time I had finished I was absolutely exhausted. I would flop out, plonk my feet into a bowl of Epsom salts and just let them soak for half an hour – a wonderfully relaxing way to finish the day.

On our opening night in Boston I was one big ball of panic. Most performers believe it's healthy to be nervous – it keeps the adrenalin flowing and makes you push yourself to the limit of your ability. Well, I remember standing in the wings, dressed in my beautiful, glittering costume, in a flat panic. I was sure I wouldn't remember a single step. My stomach was one giant butterfly. Why hadn't I just got a straightforward job, I thought to myself. I can remember, too, the very first time I ever performed on stage, I made the director set me up before the curtain rose, because I was sure I wouldn't find the courage to walk on – and in that way I couldn't get off!

Subsequently it was marvellous, of course, being a success on Broadway in *My One and Only*. The show has given me the chance to develop my career as a dancer and actress. Mind you, I was lucky to get my first acting break in *The Boy Friend*. Really, it was one of those wonderful, improbable things that happen because somebody is gunning for you. I was twenty-one and, although I hadn't been modelling for the previous two years, I was still thought of as a model. I had been to see a stage revival of *The Boy Friend* with Ken and Shirley Russell and the fashion illustrator Erté. It was Ken's birthday. Afterwards, we went out to dinner and someone said what a wonderful role that would be for me. Well, I just laughed and didn't really think any more about it. Then when I saw Ken the next week he said: 'You know, it's a good idea! Let's do a musical together – you star and I'll direct!' Well, we laughed at that and again I didn't think any more about it. But two days later Ken phoned and said, seriously, that it was an idea worth considering and would I be interested?

It seemed a crazy notion to me – the role involved dancing and the only real dancing I had ever done was as a teenager in discos. But I do believe in seizing your opportunity, and even though then I couldn't imagine myself as the star of the show, I wasn't going to turn him down without having a go! So I said yes, I'd love to.

MGM freaked out when Ken told them he wanted to use me. Well, you can see their point – to them I was the skinny model who could strike poses in front of a camera. So it wasn't surprising that shrewd business people thought it an absurd idea to gamble large sums of money on my being able to sing and dance. But Ken, bless him, said he wouldn't do it without me, and once he gets a bee in his bonnet, that's it – so in the end MGM had to agree. It was only then that Ken turned to me and asked: 'Can you sing and dance?' And I had to say: 'No, not really.' Daft, isn't it? But Ken was practical and just said I must get some lessons. He didn't seem bothered. So that's exactly what I did. While he spent nine months shooting another film, I had dance lessons with Gillian Gregory at the Dance Centre in London. A first-rate teacher, she was very straightforward in her approach and once I had got over that feeling of being 'only a model' my confidence grew alongside my ability.

Tap dance has such a strong rhythm and form that once you've learned a few steps you can put together a little routine and feel like Fred Astaire! I also went to jazz and ballet classes. Ken insisted on the ballet, not because it was needed for the film, but because he said it builds up your muscles and gives you the necessary strength for long dance routines. That made sense but I found it very hard work. I'd never done anything which involved such stretching and pulling of the muscles. But I'm glad I persevered. It taught me a lot about the way the muscles in the body work and about maintaining my balance and appearing graceful.

Many people have inhibitions about learning to dance. They think themselves too large, too tall or too ungainly. But this really is wrong as dancers come in all shapes and sizes. Karen Tamburelli says that just about anyone can learn and those with reasonable agility, co-ordination and a sense of rhythm can become quite good at it.

I see so many benefits to dance that I've become like one of those people standing on soap boxes at London's Hyde Park Corner, spreading the Word! Far more people should try it. Not only will you become fitter, but you will learn self-expression and creativity. Most exercise routines consist of a set range of actions, but with dance you can improvise and create wonderful free-form steps.

DANCING IS GOOD FOR YOU

I HAVE never been exactly fat and when I look back at some of my modelling pictures I reckon you could mistake me for a tooth-pick! But I did notice in my twenties that my thighs were beginning to get a bit puckered and slightly loose. Now they are rock-hard and a much better shape. In fact, my entire body is in better shape. I am not as skinny and through regular dance sessions have developed firm, tight muscles and a lot more curve to my body than when I was leading a less physically-demanding life. Others I know have achieved the reverse – become far slimmer and more streamlined through dancing. It's a terrific form of exercise because you are having to use just about every part of your body.

Where Can I Learn?

Where you go to learn depends on what you wish to achieve. If you ancing and are prepared to spend a bit of money, it might be worth really proficient at dhaving private lessons as well as, say, a couple of group classes each week. In this way you will make quite rapid progress. But the majority of people want to dance for pleasure and to make themselves fitter, in which case you would do best to go to one of the centres or studios which seem to have sprung up in most towns. Classes, usually lasting about an hour, are held in most kinds of dance. I think the Pineapple Studios in London and New York, owned by Debbie Moore, are excellent. They have very good facilities, top-class teachers and it's possible to learn to a professional standard if you wish. Otherwise, youth centres, clubs and other organizations quite often hold dance classes, and they would probably be considerably cheaper than those in the custom-built studios – although maybe of not as high a standard.

It is well worth visiting several different classes before you decide which to join. The difference between a teacher who's enthusiastic and has a tremendous feel for what she or he is doing, and one who may know the steps well but does not have the same intuition, is enormous. And try asking around among friends: you may find the name of a particular studio repeatedly recommended. You could also ring one of the publications devoted to dance, to see whom they suggest.

(Opposite) **Dancing is wonderful exercise, and can and should be great fun as well, but like so many things in life, timing is everything.**

How Often Should I Attend?

You should go to a dance class twice, even three times a week if you want to become fairly proficient without taking several years over it. But clearly this is a lot for most people and may prove expensive. So if the most you can manage is once a week, try to organize a time of day when you can put in at least fifteen minutes' practice. Obviously the more you practice, the quicker your skill will develop – and the quicker, too, your body will improve.

What Should I Wear?

The most popular dress is leotards, worn with tights and leg warmers when the weather is colder. I have a selection of leotards ranging from very plain, long-sleeved ones to those with low necks, short sleeves and very high-cut legs. Leotards and dance 'gear' generally – ultra short skirts, loose trousers and tops – can be found in most dress shops and boutiques nowadays. But don't rush out and buy your dance outfits until you are quite certain you will stick with it.

Seek the advice of your teacher on what shoes to wear.

TYPES OF DANCE

Tap Dancing

Tap dancing can be traced back to the American South in the early eighteenth century where the traditional dancing of the European immigrants – Lancashire clog dancing and the Irish jig – combined with the rhythmic movements of the black slaves. It was the street dance of its time – the eighteenth-century equivalent of today's body-popping and break-dancing. In those days, nails and bits of tin were attached to ordinary leather shoes or clogs.

It wasn't until the days of black jazz in New Orleans and Harlem at the beginning of the century that tap became well known. This era produced such people as Bill Robinson, John Bubbles and Buck Washington. Fred Astaire – internationally famous from the 1930s onwards with Ginger Rogers – is considered the first white man to make tap popular, and he was the first to syncopate a rhythm.

(Opposite) **Splash, splash, quick, quick, splash. The water sequence from** My One And Only.

The right music is vital in tap – Count Basie and Errol Garner records are particularly good to learn to. You can start at any age and it is not necessary to be especially fit. A good ear for beat and rhythm is useful and once you have mastered the basics you can improvise yourself. There are no hard and fast rules about what you should do with your feet. The idea is to experiment. You don't need to wear any special clothes, other than tap shoes of course. But you should be able to borrow some at your class until you decide whether you want to carry on.

Derek Hartley, who teaches at the Pineapple Studios in London, says that after a course of one, or preferably two, lessons a week for three months, and some practice in between, you can be proficient. After a year it should be possible for you to master some quite intricate routines. It will shape up your legs and ankles and generally make the body more flexible.

Ballet

Ballet (meaning 'little ball') originated in France in the seventeenth century when life was elaborate and Court rules strict under Louis XIV. It derives from folk and Basque dancing, and the very controlled foot positions date from those days when the shoes worn at Court were so elaborately adorned with jewels and embroidery that it was difficult to move around without hindrance! From France ballet found its way, via Italy, to Russia, and it was there at the end of the nineteenth century that classical ballet was created. Pavlova was the first truly international ballet dancer.

Can anyone do ballet? Teacher Maryon Lane explains that if you want to be a professional dancer, you must start young, but if you are just taking it up for pleasure and because it's a good form of exercise for the body, you may begin at any age so long as your body is reasonably strong. It tones up every muscle in the body and is especially beneficial for flabby thighs, and will tighten the front, back and sides of the thighs. It also hones leg muscles, strengthens knees and generally keeps the body flexible.

Belly Dancing

Belly dancing originated from the Middle East and Africa where it developed from the primitive tribal dances used in fertility and initiation rites. The gyrating hips and undulating movements have always suggested physical stimulation and from earliest times belly dancing has been associated with harems and exotic women. Belly dancing was introduced to Paris at the turn of the century by a dancer called Fareda, who was considered then to be very shocking. Its associations with cabaret and nightclubs continued until about twenty-five years ago when the Americans realized the beneficial, healthy qualities of belly dancing, and it has since become a very fashionable form of exercise and enjoyment.

Can anyone belly dance? Yes, anyone – young or old, male or female, fat or thin – can enjoy and benefit from belly dancing. Not only is it fairly easy to master with a bit of practice, it is also great fun for those who like to dress up and experiment with bizarre clothes and sultry make-up. Teacher Tina Hobin's pupils raid the Oxfam shops for old evening wear, colourful scarves and beads to create their costumes. To become fairly proficient at belly dancing you'll need to attend one or two classes a week (two hours in all) and practise in front of the mirror at home in between times. It takes a lot of concentration, particularly to start with, but eventually the movements will become familiar.

Belly dancing movement stimulate and massage the body's internal organs, so anyone who suffers with back, heart, lung or digestive disorders can benefit from this safe and easy form of exercise. The breathing techniques and muscle control improve the circulation and relieve tension. It will tone up the whole body, tighten the tummy, and strengthen the back and legs.

Pregnant women will find that regular belly dancing will be particularly helpful since the pelvic rocking movements actually stimulate the baby and widen the sub-pubic arch, which should assist the birth, especially if the squatting position is used. Consequently Middle Eastern and North African women call belly dancing the 'birth dance'.

Tap started out as the eighteenth-century equivalent of today's body-popping and break-dancing. Or so they tell me!

WARM-UP

THIS is a good warm-up routine before a dance session, but could be performed on its own on a daily basis to keep the body in trim.

1 Side Stretch

This is a good exercise to start with – it stretches the whole body from toes to fingertips.

Standing with feet slightly apart, tummy and bottom tucked in, stretch your right arm up and then your left arm. Repeat 8 times.

Bend forward and lightly bounce your arms down to the floor 8 times. Don't force yourself further than is comfortable and remember to keep tummy and bottom tight.

Repeat these two exercises on 4 beats, then 2, and then single beats. That should get the circulation moving well and you should then feel ready to move on to the next.

2 Back Stretch

Standing with legs straight about a foot apart, bend slowly forward with the back flexed, arms behind, palms and chin up. Stretch the body forward as far as you can and flex the lower back 8 times. Come up slowly.

Then, this time with feet together, repeat.

3 Rib Cage

Stand with your feet slightly apart. Clasp your hands behind your back and rest them lightly on your bottom. Contract the tummy muscles and tighten your bottom. Lift up the rib-cage and push it forward. Push chest and chin forward and stretch your arms back at the same time. Count up to 4, then relax. Repeat 4 times.

4 Waist Stretch

Stand with feet apart, tummy and bottom in. Bend over to the right with your left arm over your left ear and stretch 8 times. Repeat on the left side. Bend forward and flex lower back 8 times, then lean backwards and repeat. Repeat the whole movement again to 4 beats, 2 and single beats.

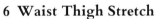

5 Tummy Tightener

Lie on your back on the floor. Keeping your tummy in, raise the right leg, point and flex the toes. Lower leg slowly to the ground. Do this exercise 8 times and then repeat with the left leg. Finally, raise both legs from the ground slowly and then lower them to the count of 8. Repeat 8 times.

6 Waist Thigh Stretch

Lie on your right side and cradle your head in your right arm. Raise your left leg as far as you can and lower. Do this 8 times. Sit up on your elbow and repeat. Then stretch your arm and repeat again. Turn on to your left side and start again.

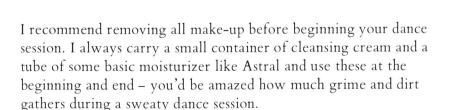

I recommend removing all make-up before beginning your dance session. I always carry a small container of cleansing cream and a tube of some basic moisturizer like Astral and use these at the beginning and end – you'd be amazed how much grime and dirt gathers during a sweaty dance session.

156

RELAXATION

THIS final chapter is mainly about ways of unwinding and coping with pressure, but first of all I want to say something briefly about a very important part of my life which often adds to those pressures. Any parent will know what I mean!

Having a child is certainly not in itself a way to calm your lifestyle or achieve inner tranquillity. Almost everyone I know has found it a shock to the system, much more demanding and exhausting than he or she imagined it was going to be. All the more important, then, to find ways of relaxing and recharging the batteries.

It was while I was pregnant that I began to think it was necessary to have a calm centre to my life. I was very conscious of the baby growing inside me; it fascinated me, and I spent lots of time sitting quietly, wondering what life was like inside. I wanted to enjoy the actual birth, and so I went to relaxation classes where I learned techniques that have been useful under other circumstances.

Reckless Rat, Artful Owl, of Captain Beaky fame, and a friend.

When Carly was born I felt very changed, very much surer of who I was and what I wanted than I had. I think many people find having a child is such a profound experience that it does alter their values. For instance, when I was younger, I was always on the go, and didn't bother too much about looking after myself because I wasn't in the frame of mind to sit and concentrate on things like decent food and ways to look after my body. Pregnancy made me do that, and afterwards I lost interest in people living glamorous lives – all that seemed absurdly superficial.

I felt very contented and relaxed, especially during the period after Carly's birth when we lived in California and I didn't work. I spent day after day in jeans and a shirt, so as not to have to worry about the baby spoiling my clothes. It seems to me that it's necessary to work out *how* you want to enjoy motherhood, being prepared to make little compromises such as mine about wearing very easy clothes, in order to feel relaxed. My advice to anyone having a baby is to take time off if you can – several months if possible – and just involve yourself in being a mother and *enjoying* this new little person. If and when you finally have to hand over to someone else for periods, it is well worth taking the time to find someone you really do feel happy about. For Carly I always choose nannies whom I like, and who would be nice to have as friends – and Carly's now old enough to have her say, too. When I travel she always comes with me – I can't bear the idea of being away from her for long, exhausting though travelling with a young child can be. But the rewards are so much greater than the stresses that it's all worth while. And, of course, I've learned *how* to relax. I'm not going to describe all the things I do for relaxation in my spare time – everyone enjoys a range of activities – but to tell you about a number of tricks I've found which have proved very useful on different occasions. A lot is written about stress and tension, with their unpleasant symptoms and side effects; one of the most effective ways of countering them is by unwinding before things get too bad. Of course the catch is that if you are really under stress then you don't feel able to relax. I have tried telling myself, when I reach this state, just to let go – but my body feels taut and I get grumpy, low and tired. I get even more tense worrying about not being able to relax!

Stress and tension tend to make us feel weary, listless and as though we need rest – when in fact what we need is exercise! This will not only loosen up the body but also unlock the mind. I know that when I'm dancing, although I get physically tired, I nearly always feel good at the end.

(Opposite) **Unwinding. An open look into an open book.**

Walking and Running

Walking and running are two very simple forms of aerobic exercise which – if you do them comfortably rather than pushing yourself too hard – can be pleasantly calming and refreshing. You need to move quite briskly to get the blood circulating, but that's about all. I have always enjoyed walking and if I have a quiet period when I'm not working I take Carly out of town somewhere where we can stride along together for an hour or so, breathing in lungfuls of clean air, and then we go home ready for a good tea.

I walk on my own, too, particularly when I feel bottled-up, jaded, cross or low in spirits. If I haven't got much time I go for a walk wherever I am – the surroundings don't really matter – though if the area isn't very attractive it helps to have something in particular to think about. One friend sets herself a poem to learn on each walk – she has a wonderful repertoire now! I work through things stored up in my mind which I haven't had time to think out properly or which are causing me a little niggling worry, step out purposefully without stopping for about half an hour and by the time I get home I almost always feel better.

To enjoy your walk it is important to wear comfortable shoes that support your feet, and to wear light clothes. I've seen people set out in high heels and big heavy coats – no wonder they come back, moaning, after about ten minutes. If you don't enjoy walking because you're unsuitably dressed, then you'll soon be making even short journeys by bus or car – so missing easy opportunities of fitting a bit of exercise and relaxation into your day. I'm sure that people bottle themselves up by being static all the time, and that a lack of exercise leads to depression and a build-up of tension.

Walking is undoubtedly good for you. It helps the circulation, increases your heartbeat if you walk briskly, and gently conditions the body, helping it to stay supple.

I am not a dedicated runner – there's no way I'd go into training for a marathon – but I do love to run around a big open area, or through grassy fields or barefoot along a sandy beach. However, I know a lot of people who go for a run of several kilometres every day – and they say they feel great on it, telling me that it not only gives the body a good airing and keeps them fit but that there's something very exhilarating about the sense of speed and the feeling that all your body is working like a well-oiled machine. On the physical level, they claim, they have improved vigour – and they can eat what they like without worrying because the body tends to ask for what it needs; on the

(Opposite) **Eyes down for a full house. You have to put your back into your exercises.**

emotional level it diminishes anxiety and helps lift depression, while on the intellectual level it sharpens the mental processes so that solutions to problems can be devised and creative ideas occur. (The explanation they put forward for this is that the exercise increases the level of oxygen in the blood, and this benefits the brain as well as the body.) In fact, for those who enjoy it, running has all the benefits of walking – only more so!

If you walk or run as a matter of course during your day you will probably find that stress and tension are not much of a problem – unless, of course, you have a major worry or anxiety. If that's the case you'll need to get it sorted out before anything can truly relax you.

Swimming

You may not immediately think of swimming as an aerobic exercise, but it definitely does get the heart and lungs working well, and helps to build up bodily strength and flexibility. To my mind it is perhaps the very best combination of activity and relaxation – the water is soothing, the motions are rhythmic while being at just the right level of physical demand, and a steady breast stroke can become almost like a meditative exercise.

Most of us swim during the summer holidays and people often say how good it makes them feel, how they will definitely keep it up when they get home – but then they find it difficult to make time for it. Swimming regularly (perhaps 15 minutes or half an hour three or four times a week) is very good for your body, toning up muscles and flattening the tummy, and it's great for relaxing the whole of you. While going to a local pool may not be as glamorous as dipping into a sunlit holiday sea or a luxurious hotel swimming pool, it is probably the only way you'll be able to swim regularly. Join a club if there is one, take out a season ticket if the pool offers it; think about meeting a friend there at lunchtime, or having a quick dip on the way to or from work – any of these strategies will help you make time for a regular swim. Most kids love it, so if you have children you can all go together. And the younger they are when they learn to swim, the safer they're likely to be in the water.

TRANQUIL RELAXATION

An entirely different approach is through yoga. People who practice yoga tell me that the combination of postures and breathing helps to bring harmony of mind and body, and they swear it is calming and quieting. Certainly, yoga has been used for thousands of years as an antidote to stress.

The Salute to the Sun is a good all round asana (posture). It affects all parts of the body including the internal organs.

Clear your mind of all thoughts and stand with your feet together and the palms of your hands together in front of your chest. (This is the so-called 'prayer position'.)

Lift your hands above your head and then return to the prayer position.

Drop your hands to your feet (if you can't touch the floor with your legs straight, then bend the knees slightly.)

Breathe in.

Stretch out the left leg and bend the right leg, keeping your chin up, back arched and fingertips by your right foot.

Breathing out lean forward with
your hands flat on the floor and
your head down.

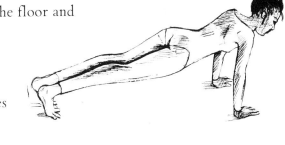

Breathe in and bring the right leg
back straight with the left leg, toes
curled.

Lift your bottom up into the air,
while breathing out.

Bend your knees, chin on the floor
and flex your back – hips raised.

Breathe in.

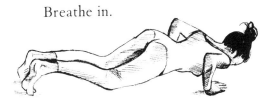

Breathing in, lower your hips and
arch the back with your hands flat
on the ground – keep your head and
chest back.
Breathing out raise your hips up
again, toes curled in and hands flat
on the floor.

Breathe in and bring your right foot
forward, chin up and lean back.
Then, breathing out, bring your feet
together and come up slowly into
the prayer position again.

For the second Salute to the Sun
reverse the sequence and stretch out
the right leg in the fifth position.

TRAVEL

Lots of people seem to look forward to going away, particularly if they don't do it very often, and then they don't enjoy the journey. This is a shame – but one of the hardest things is to arrive at the end of any trip feeling fresh and untired. I don't really understand why this is – because you're generally sitting down nearly all the way, whether you're in a car or a train or on a plane. (Of course, if you're doing the driving, that does make you tired.) But there are things you can do to help yourself, even if you're not going far.

It's amazing what a difference it makes if you're not festooned with bags and cases. I always admire people who go on holiday with just two pieces of hand luggage – and envy them when they don't have to hang about waiting for their suitcases!

I've found it's really good if I can get the timing right. Having to rush leaves me out of breath and worried that I won't get there on time, while being much too early means kicking my heels in a departure lounge or railway snack-bar. If you think you are going to have to wait about, make sure you've got something to occupy you. Something to read, a few postcards to write (you can address and stamp them before you set off if you're really organized), some knitting if that's what you enjoy – anything that will stop you fuming. A personal stereo can be very soothing in this kind of situation.

If you're travelling with kids, especially if they're very young, you'll need to take along something for them to eat and drink, as well as something for them to play with. I wouldn't now take favourite toys on holiday, in case they get lost – and anyway the novelty of even a couple of cheap toys can help you through any unexpected delays. You'll also need something to wipe them (the kids I mean) clean – airlines give you wipes in sachets, and it's a good idea to keep one or two of these handy.

If I'm travelling overnight I like to take off my make-up, and put on plenty of moisturizer, so that my skin gets as much of a rest as it can. As well as something for a quick clean-up, it's handy to carry a toothbrush – brushing your teeth is a great way to freshen up.

Because travelling is such a grubby business, I choose what I am going to wear quite carefully. It needs to be practical, and comfortable – not too tight around the neck or waist. And too-tight jeans are out! You must have seen people hobbling off planes in agony because they've kicked their shoes off to be comfortable, and then their feet have swollen! The moral obviously is to wear comfortable shoes as well.

Really, I think the key to a relaxing journey is a bit of planning, and quite a lot of organization so that everything will go smoothly – and even if it doesn't, it won't matter too much.

You'll feel better if you can move around every now and again – in a train or plane go for a stroll along the corridor or aisle. You can even do a few simple stretching exercises from time to time. Something else that helps, especially on planes where the air conditioning can leave you feeling very dry, is to drink plenty of water to stay off the duty-free drinks. Well, perhaps just one if it's the start of your summer holidays! I think I travel better if I haven't eaten too much, and I try and avoid very meaty meals just before and during a journey.

There are some lucky people who can settle comfortably into their seats for their trip, close their eyes and nap all the way. I can't do that, but I do try and relax as much as possible. I only watch the in-flight movie if it's a film I want to catch up on, and I try very hard not to get into long intense conversations with *anyone*, whether I know them well or not. It's nice when you find you're travelling with someone who can make you laugh a lot, because then the time and miles whizz by.

They keep coming up with theories about jet lag, and it does seem to vary from one person to another. I haven't got a miracle system for avoiding it, though I find it's much worse if I'm very tired before I set off on a flight, or if I've got a really punishing schedule the other end. When I can take things easy, and just flop into bed if I need to, I never feel too bad. Sometimes, though, I get badly out of synch. If everyone else has gone to bed, but your body says it's only teatime, then I think it's best to sit down and read for a bit, or go for a swim if there's somewhere accessible, or perhaps have a nice lazy hot bath, and then go to bed anyway – otherwise I'd still be fast asleep when I should be up and doing.

It is possible to relax in the most unlikely situations. Even on stage, I could snatch the odd moment to let my muscles go limp, breathe deeply and quietly, and recharge my batteries for the rest of the show.

MASSAGE

THERE are times when your body feels so tired, tense and exhausted that it seems to be crying out for a massage. Most professional masseurs tut at the idea of waiting so long that you feel it's an 'emergency' – to get most benefit, they say, you need to go at least once a month and preferably once a week. You should try to give yourself up completely to what is happening; if your massage is for relaxation you should feel ready to fall asleep by the time it's finished. If you can give in and have a sleep, do so; otherwise just lie quietly for a few minutes, then slowly come to and pull yourself together.

I am now almost addicted to massage. I was introduced to it while I was working in New York, when I had a phase of feeling weary and tense, and my body seemed generally very taut. Tension and stress are an unavoidable part of everyday life for most of us – and clearly something that promises to overcome their effects is worth trying, though I didn't believe that massage would help me. I was amazed at how much good it did! My masseuse in New York is Christiana – she treats many of the city's notables with her version of Swedish massage, in which she is clearly very expert.

Our sessions begin with deep breathing, which forces my body to begin to relax. Then Christiana sets to work, firmly but gently, going all over my body using a light oil. As she deals with the lower back I can feel the tension easing out. I put a lot of pressure on this part when I am dancing and I think it is true that many people tighten the lower back when they are tense, so that the muscles knot. Christiana also massages the acupuncture points, and this helps release the body's energy.

Massage aims at removing tension, eliminating toxins and stimulating the circulation. It also helps to drain the lymph nodes – that is where the term lymphatic drainage comes from – and there are techniques for breaking down cellulite and for helping with the problem of water retention. A full body massage generally lasts an hour, while half that time will do for head and neck or for a massage to deal with a specific complaint.

I know that it will be difficult for some people to obtain a professional massage, but there are good 'do-it-yourself' books available, such as Ouida West's *The Magic of Massage* (Century and Delilah Communications). Team up with a friend, or with your partner – otherwise try and find a good masseur through a personal recommendation or by trial and error. How can you tell if someone is good? If, during a massage, you feel as though there is an insect crawling around your back and after it as though nothing has happened, then the massage won't have done you any good. And if the massage is agony and you emerge feeling as though your bones have all been broken, that's no good either!

It is important to realize that there are a number of different types of massage. *Swedish massage* is widely used; this is the basic variety and is very relaxing. There are *medical massages*, where a particular part of the body will be treated, and kneading may well be fairly deep. Some forms can be quite painful – *rolfing*, for instance, is almost aggressive because its aim is to unlock frozen musculature and realign the body. Other sorts, such as *shiatsu*, work on the acupuncture points. *Hellerwork* is a type of deep compression massage used to correct problems by realigning the body according to the forces of gravity and, says Roger Golten in London, it will also re-educate you into using your body in such a way that you don't fall back into bad habits. Something a little different is *aromatherapy*: the use of aromatic essential oils, extracted from plants, flowers and barks. The underlying theory is that the aromas have different effects – some soothe, some stimulate, some are healing, and so on. The oils are often used in combination with massage, which rubs them into your skin – so that you are beautifully perfumed – while releasing the aroma for you to inhale. Aromatic oils have been around for thousands of years and Daniele Ryman, the fascinating woman who trained with the famous French aromatherapist Marguerite Maury, and who now runs her own clinic in London, describes in *The Aromatherapy Handbook* (Century) how records have been found charting the use of perfumes and scented oils as far back as 4500 BC.

RELAXATION FOR CHILDBIRTH

AS I've already explained at the beginning of this chapter, when I was pregnant I was very concerned that having a baby should be a good experience, and I wanted to be able to cope as well as possible when it came to the birth. So I found out about different birth methods and decided on psychoprophylaxis – a method devised in the 1950s by a man called Fernand Lamaze. Like yoga, it combines exercise and breathing. Lamaze, like Grantly Dick-Read in Britain before him, knew that most women had a conditioned reflex at the idea of childbirth – they were scared. And once you are scared you become tense, tight and this of course interferes with childbirth. His method is designed to help women not to feel frightened, and

The still before the storm. Life's never the same again, and we all thank God for that.

puts a lot of stress on relaxation and learning ways to induce relaxation. Most courses of Lamaze classes are for couples – your partner is encouraged to take part in helping you learn to relax from the beginning of the course.

Lamaze christened his method the Childbirth Without Pain movement, because he saw such heartening results in the women he prepared. You should begin at least eight weeks before the birth date of your child and do look for a good instructor. In Britain, classes with similar aims are run by the National Childbirth Trust; contact them or any other active birth organization, women's magazine or publication dealing with parenthood to ask for recommendations.

The exercises are designed to strengthen and build the body, though they are not necessarily a rehearsal for what you will be doing in labour. For example, I recall the tailor's stretch where I sat on the floor and placed the soles of my feet together in front of me and then pulled my feet towards me close to my body. With hands on my knees I pressed down towards the floor (if this is not possible you put hands on the ankles) – this helped stretch and strengthen important muscles. Try it – you'll see what I mean.

Then there was the range of special exercises for helping to cope with labour. And there were breathing exercises teaching you to use slow, rhythmic, deep chest breathing first and to move to shallow panting as contractions speed up and peak. During the classes I wondered if all of this would really help – and on the day it did.

S L E E P

I KNOW how important sleep is to me. If I don't get enough, or if I am sleeping badly, I become low and unenthusiastic about things; I find it hard to have fun with Carly and to be patient and interested in all the things she wants to share with me. My looks are also affected – I get very pale, I get bags under my eyes and my hair becomes lacklustre. Generally, I do try hard both to get enough sleep and to get the right kind of sleep.

We all *need* sleep. The effects of sleep deprivation have been recorded – some interesting research in America showed how children who were falling behind at school caught up quickly when they were allowed to sleep as often as they felt like doing. And, when their sleep quota increased, depression was lifted in adults who were getting only a few hours' sleep a night. Then there were the women who had been to their doctors with symptoms of exhaustion, saying they felt run down and nervous;

they were ordered to get more sleep and after it they all reported that they felt much better.

I know when I was working on Broadway I had to get enough sleep because I was using up all my body's energy, its resources. Most of the time, because I was physically very tired, I just fell asleep with no trouble. But I did have a time when I had things on my mind and I didn't sleep at all well – that was horrific.

A lot of people take the line that there's little you can do if you are an insomniac, but that really isn't true. A lot of work has been done in sleep clinics demonstrating the success of different methods of treatment and I have here some ideas which have proved successful with plenty of people, and they all make sense. The idea is to approach bed in a state of physical fatigue and mental peace. It is far better to be able to do it yourself than to have to reach for the sleeping pills. They may be useful in breaking a patch of chronic insomnia, but they have a way of becoming addictive – and remember they won't solve the problem.

First you need to work out *why* you are not sleeping. There could be so many different causes: the temperature of your room, the type of mattress or pillow you have, the noise in your room at night, the decor, the state of your bedroom, can all affect whether you go to sleep in a relaxed state. So, as a starter, if you are not sleeping well check through to see if perhaps your room is too hot or whether you wake up feeling chilly and all huddled up. Do you get a stiff neck because your pillow goes into lumps? Is your mattress too soft? This is far more often a cause of insomnia than the mattress being too hard! It may take a few nights to get used to, but a firm mattress will offer more support and comfort once you have grown accustomed to it.

Next, consider what and when you eat. It is not sensible to eat a big, rich meal late at night – it could well keep you awake. While doing the show in New York, I tended not to eat till afterwards. This was late, of course, but then I only ate a light meal. For example, I might have a plate of pasta with fresh herbs and a few vegetables – a meal which is easily digested, yet I did not wake up with a hungry feeling because, as I explained in the chapter on diet, pasta is slowly absorbed into the system and provides an energy flow over quite a long period. But don't eat a meal so light or so lacking in protein that you wake up mid-way through the night with a grumbling stomach. It is not sensible to eat a lot of sweet food just before going to bed as this, too, may disturb your sleep.

The best diet for good sleep is the diet which is best for your body – a small but regular amount of nutritional food, plenty of fruit and vegetables and foods which keep your bowels functioning well. Avoid stimulants – coffee is particularly bad and many people react to caffeine by being stimulated and wide awake. Ordinary tea also contains caffeine and should be avoided last thing at night. Some people find wine very relaxing in which case a glass before bed might be a nice idea. Others find it has the reverse effect and makes them wide awake – if this is how you react, avoid drinking much in the evenings.

Plenty of people find a nightcap a soothing end to the day – Teddy Roosevelt apparently liked a shot of cognac in a glass of milk, but a nightcap doesn't have to be alcoholic. Here are a few ideas:

Mix the juice of one lemon and one orange in a glass with two tablespoons of honey and top the glass up with warm water.

Drink a glass of buttermilk at at bedtime – it contains lots of calcium which is known to be good for sleep.

Warm milk is a popular nightcap either on its own or with a teaspoon of honey, molasses or malt.
But be sure it is not too hot as this may prevent rather than induce sleep.

Herbalists recommend several drinks to provoke soothing sleep. Catnip tea, camomile tea, lime blossom tea are all said to be good for relaxing you and inducing drowsiness. Decide which you like the taste of best, and drink a cup of warm infusion at bedtime.

INDEX

CREDITS

Twiggy and Robson Books are grateful to all those who supplied clothes and accessories for the photographs for this book. On the cover, facing the title page and on p 27 Twiggy is shown wearing her own blue checked shirt; on pp 7, 134–140 and 160 a body stocking by Mary Quant and for the Nylon Hosiery Co and a mini-skirt and footless tights from Pineapple Dance Centre. On pp 14, 29, 71 and 80 she wears a black skinny top by Barbara Hulanicki and diamond stud earrings from De Beers, with a hat by Quasi Modo on pp 14 and 71. The pink leather two-piece on pp 15 and 28 is also by Quasi Modo, the leather jodhpurs on p 17 by Hector of New York with an antique blouse from Shirley Russell's collection at The Last Picture Frock. The yellow suede jacket on p 18 is by Maxfield Parrish. On p 32 she wears shoes by Manuolo Blahnik and shorts by Body Map. On pp 49 and 52 a towelling bathrobe by Margaret Howell with a matching towel by Conran as turban; on pp 57 and 106 a laced corselet top by the Emmanuels and diamond stud earrings from De Beers, on p 63 a Cariocca swimsuit, on p 79 a cotton vest top by Laurence Corner, on p 105 her own wrap and on pp 108 and 127–133 her own sweater and trousers. On pp 116 and 156 she wears a silk pyjama top by Nigel Preston and on p 159 a fair isle sweater by Edina Ronay.

The photographs listed above were taken specially for *Twiggy: An Open Look* by John Swannell, with Barbara Daly or Twiggy doing the make-up and hair by Debbie Fowler of Daniel Galvin. These photographs are the copyright of Robson Books and may not be reproduced except by permission of the publishers in writing. Other photographs come from the author's own collection.

The author and publishers are grateful to the following for kind permission to reproduce:
Camera Press 42, 65; also 68, 69, 70 (by Justin de Villeneuve); Kenn Duncan 91, 142, 167; Honda 24, 115; Peter Knabb and Marshall Ward 156; Harry Langdon Photography 20, 58, 66, 141/D.P.A.; Mercury 32; National Film Archive 88; The Photo Source/Keystone 23; Rex Photos 97; David Secombe 33; Scope 25 (large photo); Martha Swope 144, 149, 150; Syndication International 170; Topham 31, 157; YTV 153.

Thanks to Macdonald & Co for permission to reproduce two recipes from Clare Maxwell-Hudson's *Your Health and Beauty Book*, to Celia Wright for the Three-Day Eating Plan and to the Vegetarian Society for the Seven-Day Diet.